This memoir of a fictional heroine, Xiac against the dramatic events of twentieth cei ing up in Beijing, she experiences the Cultu the Stars Art Movement, which changed the of China. Weaving real events and the Stars artists (including Ai Weiwei) with the fictional, this moving story shines a light on the internal workings of China and gives us an engaging heroine who rises above oppression to discover love, hope and success.

***Frank Sieren**, bestselling author, documentary film maker and Asia specialist. He has been living in China since 1994. The Times calls him one of the "decisive China authorities."*

I love your story. I just finished reading it. I couldn't stop reading it until I finished it. What I found fascinating, is the courage of the heroine to endure so many hardships. My father left China before the Communist Party of China took over the government but I heard from him so many painful stories that reminded me of Little Winter's life. Being born in the West, I was another "Sarah", feeling a bit ashamed of my ancestral roots. Brushstrokes in Time speaks to me personally. I can hear my mother's voice and my grandmother's voice in Little Winter. Your dedication and your inspiration in telling this story may bring more understanding about Chinese values and culture to the younger generation. I am honoured to endorse your book.

Yangchin Li

I think it is wonderful. It is a very beautiful story, well told and in a very appropriate and enchanting voice.'

***Michael Smith**, best-selling author of Station X, The Debs of Bletchley Park and Foley the Spy Who Saved 10 thousand Jews. etc.*

Brushstrokes in Time is charming, captivating, educational, gripping, evocative, heart rendering, challenging, inspiring, historical, interlinks the generations and their differences - calls for that which is best and highest in human nature and so much more. Today I could not put it down till I'd finished. The unusual format works well. It is a story that must see the light of day.

***Tonia Cope Bowley**, South African author, academic and founder of the Thembisa Trust.*

Huge thanks to Brushstrokes in Time. It enabled me to know more about China which otherwise in all probability I wouldn't have known.

Sushma Gaba, *Mumbai*

Having grown up in Singapore as a third generation Chinese, modern China was distant and unfamiliar to me. I only learnt about the Chinese Cultural Revolution long after the event, via brief TV references and the occasional historical article in magazines. Some Singaporeans had relatives in China and through them one got the feeling that life was hard, limited in scope and little valued by their dictators. If I had wanted to know more I then needed to look up dry, historical commentaries. However, with Brushstrokes in Time I found for the first time a fresh, unorthodox, approachable and completely enthralling novel, dealing with this complex period up till 1994. It is unorthodox because Brushstrokes is written by an English woman, Sylvia Vetta, using the voice of a Chinese refugee. Brushstrokes lays out with great humanity and authenticity, the huge panorama of events that engulfed the lives of masses living in China. All the elements of "regular life", but especially of those in the artistic movement, were researched then encapsulated in the story of one fictional woman, Xiao Dong and her friends. By its simple yet compelling story-telling, this book has taught me so much about a country that not only shaped my ancestors, but was so completely at odds with the paths taken by Diaspora Chinese living overseas. For anyone seeking to understand the China of today – especially its people – this book is essential reading.

Sian Liwicki

A hauntingly powerful debut novel reminiscent of Wild Swans. Little Winter's story takes us from Beijing to Berkeley, California by way of the Stars' Art Movement . Little Winter's story is a window into the Chinese world of the seventies and eighties about which as yet, little has been written. Truth is often best told through fiction and Sylvia Vetta's story tells it in spades.

Linora Lawrence Chair, *Oxford Writers Group*

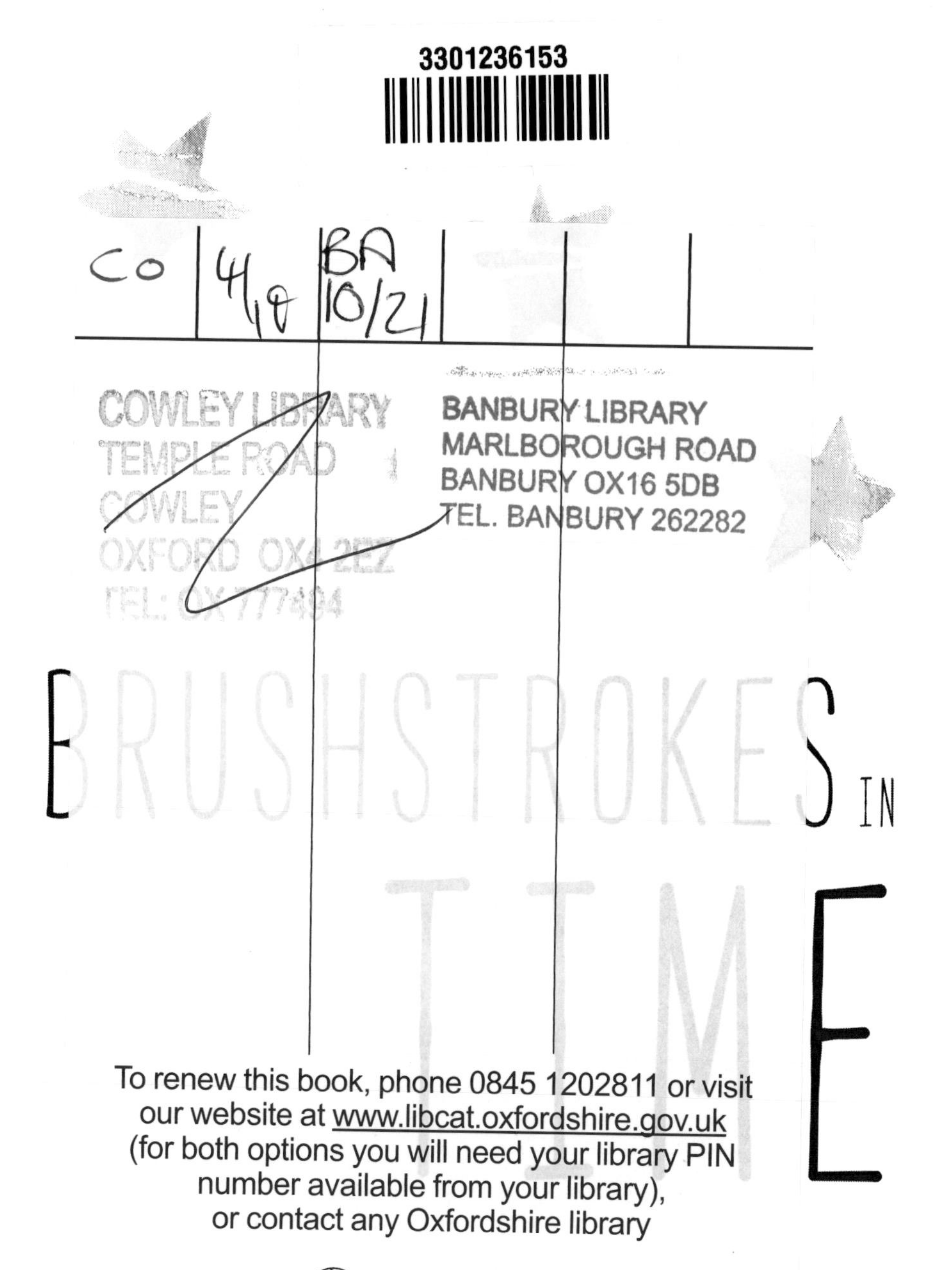

BRUSHSTROKES IN TIME

BY SYLVIA VETTA

CLARET PRESS

Cover design and typesetting by Petya Tsankova

ISBN paperback: 978-1-910461-09-9
ISBN ebook: 978-1-910461-10-5

A CIP catalogue record for this book is available from the British Library.
This paperback or the ebook can be ordered from all bookstores and from Claret Press, as well as eplatforms such as Amazon and ibooks.

www.claretpress.com

I would like to dedicate Brushstrokes in Time to the Stars artists who inspired it and to anyone anywhere in the world who campaigns for freedom of expression.

The brush and ink should follow the time …

Shitao, circa 1674

Acknowledgements

This story has been a long time in the making. In 1965 my history lecturer, Donald Tranter, introduced me to Chinese history, which was somewhat unusual for the time. The new topic of study captivated me and, when Chairman Mao launched the Cultural Revolution in 1966, I bought a copy of his *Little Red Book* and immersed myself in it. Six months later, disturbing footage of teachers being humiliated appeared on our news. I learned to be wary of idealistic speeches. I learned to think for myself.

My interest in China continued through the years. Since 2001, it has been my privilege to review exhibitions on behalf of The Oxford Times. Few have made as strong an impression on me as the first show at The Ashmolean Museum by a living Chinese artist. In 2005 Qu Leilei's *Everyone's Life is an Epic* consisted of 21 striking contemporary portraits. Each subject had been asked to describe his/her philosophy of life. Under his portrait, a homeless man had written 'You are not a failure until you give up trying' and his chiselled features were surrounded by bold colour with the Chinese translation in calligraphy that was integral to the work. East and West had met in this brush.

Chris Gray, the arts editor, commissioned me to write a profile feature on the artist and I learned first-hand of the epic life that was Leilei's. I listened to his stories about The Stars Art Movement, of which he was one of the five founders. I visited Beijing when Qu Leilei was there. He took me to the Chinese National Gallery and showed me the railings where these brave artists had hung their controversial pictures in 1979. The artists, poets and democracy activists knew each other and were part of the on-going process of opening China to new ideas and new ways of living, and they risked life and limb to do so. Art was instrumental in opening China to free speech, public criticism, and self-expression. I was surprised that so few people outside China knew about The Stars and their art movement although one of them, Ai Weiwei has become a star throughout the world. The Chinese Government's desire to shield its population from knowledge of the events in Tiananmen Square in 1989 means that a Chinese writer is unlikely to write a book like *Brushstrokes in Time*, so this English writer wanted to share the story of The Stars, the start of the Democracy Movement and what happened next.

I spent much of 2005-2010 interviewing, reading and visiting China to research this book. Some of the characters in this novel are real; a list of the political figures is at the back. The narrative post 1983 is solely a result of my own research and imagination, as is Little Winter's and Hu Weiwei's love story. Any errors are solely my responsibility.

Although Jung Chang's Wild Swans helped us feel what it was like to live through the turbulence of The Cultural Revolution, and Ma Jian's *Beijing Coma* described events in Tiananmen Square in 1989, there is little accessible literature for the average lay-person about the events that took place between 1976 and 1989. It is my hope that this story helps redress that imbalance.

Author Michael Smith, Sushma Gaba in Mumbai, and South African-born academic Tonia Cope Bowley as well as a Chinese acquaintance were the first to read an early version of this novel and they encouraged me. I want to thank Mary Lucille Hindmarch who introduced me to Claret Press and its Editor-in-Chief, Katie Isbester, whose skill, hard work and patience has honed this novel and made it publishable. I'm honoured and grateful to the distinguished people who have endorsed *Brushstrokes in Time*.

An especial thanks to all my family and friends who have shown great patience and forbearance with me during the ten years in which this novel has evolved.

Table of Contents

Foreword by Dr. Maria Jaschok

Part 1: The Void 1

Part 2: The Dragon Years 59

Part 3: Art and Love 87

Part 4: Despair 139

Part 5: Exile 165

Epilogue: The Changing Face of China 183

Political Figures Mentioned in Brushstrokes in Time 185

Foreword

I read the manuscript with different points of view in mind, needing to satisfy myself on historical accuracy, political perspicacity, cultural sensitivity and, not least, the characterization of the main protagonist, the narrator Xiaodong (Little Winter), as a convincing, believable and complex creature born of her history and family. I consider that the writer has succeeded in meeting all of these benchmarks, providing moreover a deeply informed portrayal of the little-known, important Stars Art Movement and its part in the short-lived experiment in 1976/9 in Chinese intellectuals' exercise of democratic rights of free speech and dissent. The insertion of a fictitious character, Xiaodong, into descriptions of the fate of actual members of the Star Arts Movement is surprisingly successful – surprising because a character created by a western author to evoke the volatile relationship between Chinese politics and the arts through most personally-felt experiences could have so easily gone awry, felt forced and artificial. That this has not happened, that the authenticity of China's contemporary artists' life and work is not compromised or, indeed exoticized, is testimony to the quality of writing. Moving yet never mawkish, informed yet entirely accessible, this book should have popular appeal and, I believe, is destined for a wide readers' market.

Professor Maria Jaschok, *Research Fellow, Director of Gender Studies, Lady Margaret Hall, Oxford University*

Dr Maria Jaschok lived in China between 1979 and 1996 - the most important period covered in the novel.

To my precious daughter, Sara

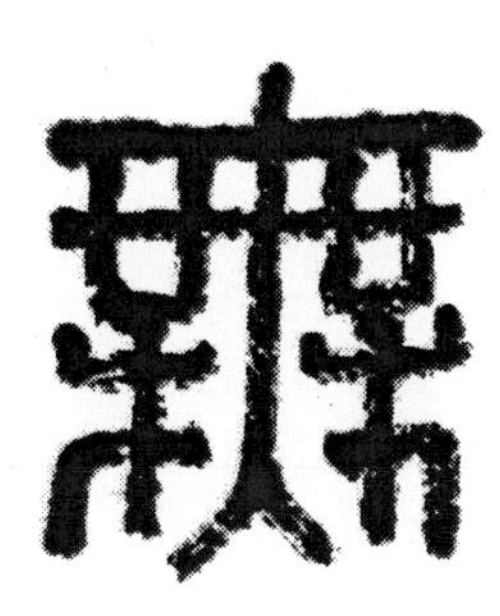

Part 1: THE VOID

Berkeley California June 2008

This is the book I struggled not to write. I buried the pain along with my Chinese name and changed my fate. But your father believes you will only understand yourself as well as me if you know my story, my journey from my childhood home on Beijing's Millionaire's Avenue to the only home you know on College Avenue, in Berkeley California.

He says that all you see is your mother, the American Winnie. When I came here, I tried to leave behind Xiaodong (in English, Little Winter). But you have worked out that beneath my façade lurks something untold. Today as I write this in 2008, in your face I see myself, Xiaodong, aged fourteen. But your name is Sara Newberry. Your father wanted to call you Su Lin because, although Chinese, it sounded like Sue Lynn which is easy for Americans to remember. I insisted on calling you Sara.

My silence about my past and your American name were intended to protect you but their effect was to exclude you. Since your fourteenth birthday you have fought me not with fists but with tantrums. Sara, you were such a sweet girl but children do not like deceit. That is why you have become sulky and I have become angry. Your father says I must write my memoir and then you will understand my black dog days and not want to hurt me. Maybe it is not your intention to hurt me but it hurts all the same when you won't speak to me or you mimic my Chinese English. Then I get into a rage - which doesn't help. It's just that I worry that my story will freeze your heart, and whatever love you might still hold for me will be erased. When you read the memoir I write for you, I hope you will understand and forgive me.

Today, I tapped out a few words on the computer. The English letters don't look right. They feel wrong. I picked up a pen and the shapes that appeared on the page look perfect. Those characters are the calligraphy of my native land. They are an art form in themselves. They look and feel like me. Sara, you may not understand these words but, even when ugly, they look beautiful. Art, poetry, calligraphy are part of who I am.

I don't read enough books, Sara. There are few new novels written in Chinese published here and I am a slow reader in English. I have not regretted that so much until now, when I have to write this memoir and have little understanding about how to do it. So I have decided to start from near the beginning and go through to the end. No frills, as you say here. Although this book may not be slick like a professional one, it is written from the heart, from mother to daughter. And that's where I will begin my story: with my mother and me, her daughter.

Beijing childhood 1962

On Friday nights, my mother would lock the door of our flat in the nineteen fifties block, constructed in the favourite building material of the time, concrete. After a forty-minute bus ride through the western suburbs of Beijing, we emerged to the sound of birds welcoming us to their earthly paradise, my father's cottage in the grounds of the old Imperial Summer Palace. My father, a senior communist party officer, worked in Fundamental, the department concerned with the development of industry, and was allowed a house in the grounds of the Summer Palace. Most weekends, my mother and I joined him there. I liked to rush ahead and skip through the opening courtyard and make for the Garden of Harmonious Interests, where the cool waters were completely hidden by brilliant green lotus leaves. This perfect playground appeared di-vine but mother said it was a man-made creation.

'The Emperor Qianlong built it as a gift for his mother. You see even the emperor respected his mother. Just remember that when you stamp your feet and pout your lips.'

She tried sounding martial and aloof but, despite the unisex clothing, nothing could disguise her feminine features and gentle nature.

Not far from the entrance, I caught the eye of the great bronze ox looking over the glistening waters of the Kunming Lake and ran my fingers over the eighty character poem carved on its body. This too was the work of the Qing Emperor whom my mother so admired. One of the poems she had written for me on the fan she gave me was by him. But in the steaming summer days, I avoided the shrewd eye of the imperial ox because I could hardly wait to plunge into the refreshing waters.

As I walked down the longest corridor on earth, decorated with classic tales of Wu Song beating the Tiger and dreamy scenes of the Red Mansion, I took a fleeting glance at the Romance of the West Chamber. Then I looked up the hill at the tiles on the sweeping roof of our weekend home. Grooved like the straight etched trunks of the pines, they seemed to merge into the landscape. The hundreds of bosses on the circular ends of the roof supports were moulded with ancient patterns. Mama pushed open the huge red lacquered door and I ran into the courtyard and father came out to greet us. He was tall for a Chinese man of that time and when he laughed he looked like a jolly Buddha; and he was laughing as he gave me a bear hug. I didn't realise how unusual he was. I thought all fathers hugged their daughters. Watching the pleasure in my parents' greetings, I even thought all husbands and wives loved each other.

On Saturday morning as soon as I had finished my little breakfast, I rushed outside. I had made friends with the boy and girl from the next courtyard house. The boy's name was Weiwei. Chinese names are given for their meaning and his meant cultured. Jia meant beautiful, but his sister Jia didn't have a regular beauty: her features were square compared with mine and her forehead was a little narrow but she, like her brother, had sparkling mischievous eyes. I thought of her as my best friend because she was such fun to be with.

I can close my eyes and hear and see clearly the three of us laughing as Weiwei persuaded us to climb onto the flat roof of an outhouse next to their weekend home. Weiwei stretched to his full height and grasped a wooden joist, pulling himself onto the yellow tiles. He reached down a hand for me and soon I stood beside him. Jia refused his help and we waited while she struggled up to join us. We shouted and laughed as we jumped from roof to roof until, short of breath, we stopped and gazed across at the sparkling lake. We turned to face Dragon Alley and swept our eyes down, along the invisible spine of the great dragon, to its end in the little island in the lake.

Towering over us was the largest building in the Summer Palace, the Fragrant Buddha Temple, with its four towers of eaves spreading a shadow over the man-made Hill of Longevity. In school, we were so proud when we learned that, after the revolution, this Imperial Playground was opened to the heirs of the labourers who built it. Now I am surprised that my ten-year-old self did not feel privileged to be there.

Jia, Weiwei and I slid down a side wall and started striding up the steep stone steps leading towards the temple. I stopped for breath and noticed the pebbles set in the path creating patterns of flowers and leaves that later that day I would draw for my father. Underneath, I would write a poem. I tried to write calligraphy with a chalk long before I understood the significance of those double strokes. I discovered that a simple brush and a block of ink were all that was needed to transform a blank page into a thing of beauty. But at ten, I was not aware that art was at the very heart of my being. Then, my feet itched to climb the trees until hunger drove me home. I struggled to open the huge door guarded by stone lions, the powerful protectors of our young lives.

Saturday lunch was eaten in the Tingli Guang, or Yellow Song Bird Hall, where emperors once dined with their court. I had an ability which I did not realise was unusual. Once I had seen a painting, I easily recreated it in my mind – so I could visualise the delicate pictures of those imperial banquets, and wondered what the emperor Qianlong would have thought of our communal canteen style meals. I filled my plate and solemnly joined my parents but Father laughed and pretended not to know about my antics with Weiwei and Jia.

I make it sound as though this were a Utopia, and in a way it was. It was my Utopia. It was the view from the longest corridor in the whole world, and the view from the Hill of Longevity. My parents treated me as a precious little jewel, and I was given everything I wanted. I pestered my parents until they bought me paints with which to colour my imagination blue and red and gold and green, like the paintings in the Long Corridor. However, not every moment was bliss. China's recent past occasionally interrupted my idyll.

Once, early in the morning, before the palace opened to visitors, we children played on the steps of the Pavilion of Precious Clouds and I ran towards the Long Corridor shouting, 'Catch me if you can.' As I turned the corner near the ferry boat wharf, I skidded to an abrupt halt. Weiwei came up behind me and stared. The man blocking the pathway was the figment of nightmares. His huge dark eyes protruded so far I imagined they could roll like marbles along the ground. In a booming voice, he asked what we thought we were doing. Shame– faced, we said sorry to the caretaker. With that, he turned and walked away leaving us riveted to the spot; our eyes fixed on a vision like nothing we had seen before. He seemed to have no separate neck; it was as if his head was glued to his body. Once he was out of sight, we made for the safety of home. My father was surprised to see us back so soon. Fear was still written on our faces so he asked what had happened.

'Ah, I see you have met old soldier Wang. Well, you must show him respect, he is a brave man.'

Weiwei's face reddened and my father asked him, 'Would you like to hear Wang's story?' We all three nodded eagerly because we loved my father's stories.

'During our struggle with the Japanese, like your mother and I, Wang joined the Red Army to free our land from occupation. You will find this story hard to believe but it is true and you have seen the evidence. His pia was sent to locate the enemy and was told to spread out in the woods that surrounded their camp. So Wang was quite alone when he came across a whole platoon of Japanese soldiers. As he turned to run, one of them swung his bayonet to decapitate him. Yes, children, they very nearly succeeded. The blade narrowly missed his spine but summoning all his strength he held his severed head in place and ran and ran and ran for five miles. Our doctors saved him but that is why the back of his head looks so strange.'

We were silent then gasped, 'Wow! He is such a hero.'

Sara, a Pia is the equivalent of a platoon. I'll try not to take it for granted that you will understand Chinese terms.

I thought of Wang in school the next day when the teacher praised revolutionary heroes. I wanted to tell her about him. Instead I learned about another hero. The teacher stood up very straight and her eyes looked at each of us in turn as she told the story of Lei Feng. She was only five-foot tall but seemed to grow by inches when she was inspired.

'Girls, this is the story of a great hero. His name was Lei Feng; he was just an ordinary soldier who came from a poor family. Soon after the death of his father, while Lei Feng was still a boy, their greedy landlord abducted his mother and raped her. Our hero vowed to avenge her. The revolution brought about the downfall of that evil man. In gratitude, Lei Feng joined the People's Liberation Army promising to sacrifice himself for others and for Chairman Mao.'

My parents called me Xiaodong, Little Winter, because I was tiny at birth and born in December when a bitter chill settles over Beijing. Because of the meaning of my name, I took particular notice at the mention of winter. My teacher praised me enthusiastically when I quickly learned to recite this poem from Lei Feng's diary.

To the commander we are as warm as spring
To the revolutionary worker we are as hot as summer
To the selfish we gust like the autumn wind
To the enemy we are as cold as winter.

So Sara, Lei Feng's ambition was to become a cog in the revolutionary machine. Our teacher said that Chairman Mao liked that so much that he wanted every Chinese to copy him!

I loved to sketch Lei Feng plunging deep into a sea of flames, all for Chairman Mao. The tongues of fire I painted seemed to burn even brighter when a shaft of sunlight settled on my picture after teacher pinned it to the wall. We were urged to be like the hero and be prepared to sacrifice ourselves for our country and our leader. Each morning, the whole school marched under the red flag singing energetic songs.

My school was Number Three Girls' School so I only got to meet boys at the weekend. That was when Weiwei told me his favourite hero was Wang Jie whose platoon was practising grenade-throwing when one landed close to his comrades. Weiwei's eyes lit up as he said, 'The hero threw himself on it, sacrificing himself so the others would live.' All our heroes seemed to write diaries. We studied them and learned whole passages by heart. Sitting here alone on this Californian hill, I can still recite,

Firstly, I am not afraid of suffering. Secondly, I am not afraid of death.

Looking up into the hills wondering how to explain my childhood enthusiasm for Chairman Mao, I think the next chapter of my belated diary must be ...

Indoctrination

Sara, it's not that there is no indoctrination in American schools. Just as we marched under the Red Flag every day, you swear allegiance to the United States under the Stars and Stripes. That's not so different. What was different was that, in

China, power was concentrated in one man's hands.

If we had been allowed to believe in God, then Mao would have been ours. We were literally awestruck by him. We were taught about the institutions of the Communist Party, of local government and democracy, yes democracy. My mother taught Russian and Russian studies at Beijing University. She made me feel part of a universal brotherhood.

MaMa said that meant sisterhood as well. When my NaiNai (father's mother) lived with us she had bound feet. I shared a bedroom with her and when she changed her bandages, I had to leave the room; the smell was so sickening. Mother explained,

'Xiaodong, that is what we we're fighting for; fighting for all the oppressed men and women of China. When your NaiNai was born, women were a thing of shame to be kept under control by men. One of the first acts of the new government was the marriage act, which gave us the right to say No. Fighting together for the revolution, men and women became equal comrades in the struggle.'

When I grew up I could see that wasn't true, men still held the reins of power but I felt determined that our generation should create the society my mother dreamed of and fought for. She had joined the communists when they were fighting the Japanese invaders. Her family sheltered some fighters trying to get back to their platoon. Someone informed on them but a brave neighbour gave warning that the Japanese were on their way to arrest them and they managed to escape with just minutes to spare.

Sara, neither of us would be alive today, if it had not been for that act of friendship.

From then on, my mother fought with the People's Liberation Army (PLA).

'Xiaodong, rights can be lost as well as won; that's why we teach you about the bad times, in the past, so you will continue the revolution.' said Ma.

I tasted the bad times in 1959, when I was seven years old and Chairman Mao proposed The Great Leap Forward. After that, I often went to bed hungry and that feeling of an empty stomach is still vivid in my memory.

At the start of The Great Leap Forward, I dashed to see the huge murals appearing on the city walls filled with romantic imagery celebrating our brave new world. It was to be a time of plenty. In one painting, the cotton grew so high that it reached into the sky and merged with the fluffy clouds. In Chinese mythology, dragons are in charge of water so another giant poster showed chained dragons. Smiling men and women directed the flow of water into man-made reservoirs and rivers to irrigate the fields. Seduced by what I had seen, I tried to copy the pictures and felt in control of a mighty dragon.

As part of this brave new world, Chairman Mao urged all farmers, hospitals and schools to make steel. A kiln was built in our playground and every day, a different class looked after it. For us children it was fun yet serious, pretending that we were grown up workers. One night, I dreamt that my school made so much steel that it filled the entire Kunming Lake and covered the Hill of Longevity, and in the morning I drew my dream. Now I know those posters were as unrealistic as my dreams. The truth lay hidden beneath those jolly images.

Mao took the land away from the peasant farmers and forced them into state-owned cooperatives where, like us school children, everyone was expected to make steel. Maintaining their little furnaces consumed the farmers' time and energy and kept them from the fields. Everywhere people cut down trees and burned furniture to feed the furnaces. Food became scarce but Mao Zedong blamed it on the birds, in particular his pet hate – sparrows! But he came up with a startlingly simple solution; exterminate them!

The boys in the back yards of our estate needed no encouragement. I hid my shame, because I loved feeding crumbs to the birds from the balcony of the bedroom I shared with grandmother. I couldn't bring myself to kill them. When handed a catapult by a friend, I carefully avoided hitting them.

'Chowy needs practice,' laughed my friends in the street. And they showed off as the unsuspecting little creatures dropped from the trees and no one reprimanded them. They were, after all, only carrying out the leader's directive. But sparrows eat insects and plagues of them survived to ravage the already depleted crops.

In Beijing, we were ignorant of the tragedy unfolding in the countryside. If anyone was aware no one really spoke about it. But even we privileged inhabitants of Beijing went hungry. At playtime, my friends and I were so famished we hunted for grasshoppers. We folded paper to create origami snappers, not for telling fortunes, but to catch bees without being stung. We ripped them apart and sucked the sweetness from their bodies. When you are really hungry it is surprising what you can do. I'll never forget the joy of going into our garden at the Summer Palace and helping mother pick bamboo shoots. I can still savour the fragrant taste of egg fried rice with the stir fried vegetables and bamboo shoots we harvested and Ma cooked during those hard times. Thirty million people died from starvation.

Eventually, the steel mania abated perhaps because the resulting pig iron was so useless that even Mao had to recognise his fad was damaging the country. Life returned to more or less normal.

When a neighbour told me that children in the West lived on the streets, were starving and had to rummage in dustbins for food, my heart went out to the poor oppressed children of the West – I knew what it was like to be hungry – and I hoped Chairman Mao could help them.

In 1962, it was time for me to leave primary school. My art teacher had introduced me to Daoist art and taught me to sketch perfect butterflies, flowers and birds. But in Middle School, landscape painting was not encouraged. I painted jolly workers, revolutionary heroes and, with great reverence, Mao himself. I discovered sport and my favourites were swimming and ice-skating. Sports School was much more than an after-school activity and the competition for places was fierce; so I was proud to get admission to train as a skater.

Three evenings a week, I took the bus to the Beijing Shi Cha Hai Sports School near to the Rear Sea for training and for special rations! One day, I swept gracefully round and round and, in my mind, my feet etched the ice with forbidden pictures of bamboo and blossom. My heart raced and I dug my blades fiercely to a halt and pulled myself together. I raised my arm and dashed forward like a flag waving comrade feeling like a patriot. I vowed to be a good comrade.

Often at the weekends the team slept over at Sports School. And there were boys! I felt shy.

Sara, you really wouldn't understand how shy we were. Our hormones were starting to rise but we could have no physical contact. We thought it adventurous just shaking hands!

Some sunny weekends we were allowed to join the swimmers and headed for Kunming Lake, in the Summer Palace. Coach encouraged us from a boat as we swam back and forth across the lake building up our stamina. Rippling along the spine of the splendid imaginary dragon from its head on King Dragon Island, we crossed the lake to the far pagoda by the Jade Belt Bridge, known as its tail.

After one of those sessions, I was so exhausted that I fell asleep by the side of the lake and began to experience watery dreams. I opened my mermaid eyes to see Liu Wang and Yao Zisheng laughing at me having pushed me into the lake. As I splashed and spluttered, I laughed too but I decided to get my own back. It is hard to overstate how reticent a good Chinese girl should be. Traditional values dominated despite the revolution. So it was almost radical when I demanded, 'For that, you owe me your dumplings.' And I ate my way through their rations! Despite our coy looks, we were positive and optimistic. Laughing together under the sun, the future looked bright and full of fun. Just as we were embarking on the selection process for the team to represent Beijing at the National Championships, strange and subtle changes to our education began.

1965: Class struggle - literally!

Until I was fourteen, I was taught in a cooperative atmosphere. And despite the spells of indoctrination we learnt most of the subjects you learn. We were unaware of the looming disaster. Perhaps we should have seen it coming because of a foretaste in 1965. I've explained how we revered Mao's words – well Mao admired Joseph Stalin and was not happy when, after his death, Khrushchev denounced him. He said there are many Chinese Khrushchevs sleeping beside us. Of course, if the Chairman said this Khrushchev was a bad lot, then he must be an enemy of our beloved Chairman Mao and so an enemy of us all. But who were these Chinese Khrushchevs? I was confused. I knew no one with that name but a teacher explained that,

'Chinese Khrushchevs are people who want to follow his example: they are Revisionists.'

At that time I was happy in my innocent adulation of Mao but now I know that Mao, fearing that revisionism could usher in his downfall, devised a plan to stay in power. He decided to divide and rule. His aim was to turn the young against the old, and even friends and family members against each other. And Sara, he succeeded.

For me the unease began with an essay all schools were instructed to set. It was entitled 'The Class Struggle in our Class'. Imagine my confusion!

'Am I meant to criticise my friends? Surely not?'

I decided to approach the subject by addressing the need to share work equally. Usually we read our essays aloud to the class but unusually this particular exercise was to be secret. A friend whispered to me that Jung had criticised me saying that I thought I was better than everyone else because I was selected for Sports School. When I told my parents, a flicker of anxiety crossed their faces but then they smiled and BaBa (Daddy) said,

'You've nothing to worry about; you're a good comrade and always share. A little advice – some people can be jealous. I know it's hard for you to reign in your enthusiasm, Little Winter, but listen first and be careful what you say.'

I found that hard to do. I tried to adapt when the style of teaching at school changed. Before, we had learned about Con Fuzi (Confucius) and Lao Tzu (Founder of Daoism) but somehow they had become class enemies. Politics took up more and more time in school. I was a conscientious student and so very determined to become a true revolutionary and use my artistic talents in the cause of equality. I set about learning Lei Feng's diary by heart. To prove yourself, this is what you must do.

To begin you needed to punish yourself.
Secondly, you had to be cruel to enemies.
Thirdly, you must seek out enemies.

This third instruction, I had interpreted as foreign enemies but not everyone thought that way. The atmosphere soured as some people began to seek out enemies amongst their neighbours. School became loud and frightening. Mimi came to school in tears, bedraggled and so different. Her lovely long hair had been roughly chopped; it looked so ugly.

'My brother denounced me as a revisionist and class enemy,' she said.

I had longed for a brother like Weiwei but for once, I was grateful I was an only child. I overheard my parents whispering about Chen Boda and Jiang Qing. Jiang Qing was Chairman Mao's fourth wife, known as Madame Mao. From then on, home changed a bit. The laughter disappeared and my parents sounded irritated with each other. After a fit of bad temper, they looked at each other with sad eyes.

Normal lessons had almost ceased when Number 3 Girls' Middle School was asked to take part in the struggle against counter-revolutionaries. At school next day, Son Bin was recruiting for a new revolutionary group. She said it was our duty to fight for Chairman Mao and destroy his enemies. I asked her if I could make posters and she looked pleased.

Now that I had something to do, school felt exciting. I painted a poster showing our valiant comrades in Cuba and Vietnam standing up to our American Imperialist enemies. Because I was good at calligraphy, Son Bin asked me to write slogans on posters and banners and we all paraded them proudly in the street.

June 13th, 1965: The nightmare begins

I arrived at school but it was nothing like your school, Sara. It was no longer a place where teachers taught children – oh no – now the children were in control. We worry when indiscipline rules in some inner-city schools, but pupils playing havoc is not government policy in the USA. So you may find my next stories difficult to comprehend.

When Mao ordered the schools to close; he didn't mean the buildings, just the learning. At first I thought,

'Great! I can train every day for a place in the national skating team – much more fun than learning politics.'

But my dreamtime was drowned out by the sound echoing around our playground: loudspeakers blasting out articles from the People's Daily.

'Now lessons are stopped,' said our leader, 'and young people are given food. With food they have energy and they want to riot. What are they expected to do, if not to riot?' Our instructions were to sing The East is Red and support the struggle for liberty, equality and fraternity.

Sara, you won't be surprised, any more than Mao was, that we teenagers, brimming with energy and enthusiasm, were keen to join in. He had turned us into workers when we made steel and now he turned us into revolutionaries and trusted us to change China.

Marching past another Middle School I saw a rather different poster to the ones I had made; it denounced not external enemies but perceived Chinese enemies of Chairman Mao. It was the work of Red Guards. I wondered: Who were these Red Guards?

Mother taught Russian and Russian literature at Beijing University. After Mao quit Beijing in November 1965, something had changed there too. Each day she came home looking tense and worried. I overheard her talking to father.

'Liu Shaoqi (The Deputy Chairman) and Deng Xiaoping (The General Secretary) think we should do something about the Big Mess.' I wasn't a good eavesdropper. Mother beckoned to me and gave me a lecture.

'Your enthusiasm is as it should be and so are students' vigour and determination but these leaders want it channelled into projects which will help people and develop our country - not into destructive activities.'

To help common sense prevail, my mother joined the working parties set up by Liu and Deng. Their plan was to win the confidence of young people by giving copies of The Little Red Book containing Mao's thoughts to each school and university student. I was so proud of my copy and set about learning all the Chairman's great thoughts by heart.

But it wasn't these leaders respected by your grandparents – people who wanted an end to the chaos on the streets – who held the reins of power. Oh no, the puppet masters wanted young people to become violent. Sara, what happened next will seem to you bizarre, like something out of Alice in Wonderland, but this is no fantasy fiction. This happened and your mother lived through it. The terms may be hard for you to understand but read on and you will discover the consequences of giving people labels.

Mao returned to Beijing in May 1966 and declared that all dissident scholars and their ideas should be eliminated – like the sparrows before them. He accused Communist officials of protecting the scholars and described them as 'those in power following the capitalist road.' Before long, his targets became known as Capitalist Roaders. Mao singled out Deng and Liu and their supporters, accusing them of wanting to 'quench the people's revolutionary fire'. One of those supporters was my mother.

At the time, I didn't understand what was happening; I was only fourteen and from birth had been taught to almost worship Chairman Mao. Looking back, I can see how astute Mao was at purging anyone he thought threatened his power. He had left Beijing on purpose, giving the opportunity for Deng and Liu and the others he fretted about to expose themselves. And of course, they and my mother had fallen into his trap.

A new, more revolutionary, power group emerged and soon the name on everyone's lips was 'The Gang of Four'. The four were Mao's wife and her colleagues, Yao Wen Yuan, Zhang Chunqiao and Wang Hongwen. Fortunately, my mother was in Shanghai when Deng and Liu, whom she admired, were attacked and arrested.

By July 1966, Mao quit Beijing again, leaving the Gang of Four to do his dirty work while he travelled to Wuhan. There, swimming the Yangtze he swam his way deeper into our hearts. The boys my age identified even more with our vigorous leader as we were urged to follow Chairman Mao through wind and waves. Naively, I thought of it literally because I loved to swim. In the water, I was not just in another element, I felt like another person, a sleek elegant creature flying like a dart with only the ripples behind me breaking the silence.

But making waves meant something altogether different to the growing bands of Red Guards. Opposing capitalist counter-revolutionary activity encouraged some of them to attack shops and destroy their antique façades.

Passing the ruin of a once beautiful building that I had often stopped to admire, I felt sad and averted my eye. As I reached home, my heart lightened at the touch of the familiar rust-red, heavy Ming-style door still intact. Home was like a refuge from the confusing events, so I half ran up the stairs brushing my sleeve on the dusty wall. At the top I stopped short: the door was unlocked and swinging open. An anxious lump rose in my throat as I crossed the threshold. It was not the home I had left that morning; books and papers were strewn over the floor, drawers were open and clothes hanging out. Pots of geraniums were smashed and their soil scattered among the debris. Then I saw father sitting with his head in his hands and I asked what had happened.

He looked up, his face rigid with anger but he didn't reply. Then I heard my mother's footsteps on the stairs. She surveyed the damage and turned towards my father. He simply said, 'Red Guards'.

They had confiscated the books they described as poisonous weeds leaving only the ones regarded as politically correct. We lost all the foreign literature, the philosophy books and most art books. Why the art books? What was wrong with them? My hands shook – I loved them like they were a part of me.

'Landscapes don't serve the people,' Father imitated the bark of determined Red Guards.

Mother saw the seals of wide tape plastered across the television set. Father responded to her gaze, 'Capitalist'.

'How could you sit there while they ransacked our home?'

She strode across the room and tore the tape from the screen. I felt awkward, this was the first time I had seen my mother angry with my father and it shocked me. It also made me feel guilty because it was my generation attacking people like them that had caused the rupture between them. Seeing my parents' hurt feelings, I felt ashamed. I worked all evening clearing up and cleaning so it began to look like our home again.

The next day, I visited a friend in the next block and couldn't believe what I saw. It was empty; the Red Guards had taken everything. My heart thumped so loudly that I thought everyone could hear it. My friend was crying. I tried to comfort her but didn't know what to say. Maybe my father did the right thing?

August 18th 1966: The trigger - the rally in Tiananmen Square

Sara, I notice you and your friends' quick-fire moods. I noticed your excitement when you went with your friends to the Justin Beiber concert last week – we were really no different. We got just as worked up, just as fast over just as little. The difference is that afterwards we burned our own culture and history.

Half-walking, half-running with cheerful groups of friends to Tiananmen Square, I had completely erased from my mind my parents' anxiety and the raid on our house. We marched through the Gate of Heavenly Peace which guards the southern approach to the Imperial Palace complex, formerly called the Forbidden City. The crowded alleys in front of the gate had been levelled and a vast empty space created surrounding one simple monument: the Monument to the Martyrs of the Revolution. Austere government buildings lined the edges; standing in the Square an individual felt like a speck of dust.

My excitement grew in intensity as more and more teenagers arrived in the square and began to fill its cavernous space. I was just one among over a million young people gathered there that day beneath the huge portrait of Chairman Mao. In Tiananmen Square, I usually felt like an insignificant pebble as it is so vast but on that day it became crowded and uncomfortable. I had no idea why we were there. I understand now that we were an epic crowd of naïve extras in one of the greatest shows on earth, a banner waving singing and chanting ocean armed with our Little Red Books gathered to celebrate the People's Republic of China.

The crowd erupted with a deafening noise as Mao himself appeared like a god before us. We went mad with revolutionary fervour. He looked solid, framed in front of his enormous portrait with the sun's rays streaming all around him. I have often thought of that day and wondered why my emotions were so powerful. To start with, the stage was the largest public square on earth. The audience must have been one of the largest anywhere at any time and all eyes were focused straight ahead. In Chinese Imperial paintings, the Emperor appears bigger and brighter than other human beings, for he is seen as the ruler of heaven. To me, as the light emanated from 'our glorious leader', I felt privileged that a ray of that light shone on me as well. His message was intended for me personally – or at least that was how it felt.

The vision before me was of Chairman Mao, as the Big Red Sun, who would enlighten the whole world. Mao rarely spoke in public so we were overwhelmed by the excitement of the occasion. In the end, he spoke just a few words and left the speeches to others. Lin Biao appeared for the first time as Mao's new deputy and he told us to leave our schools and to smash the four olds: that is, we must destroy old customs, old ideas, old culture and old habits.

With school friends, I went on the rampage. At the back of an old temple were niches filled with little statues of Buddha. Over-excited we smashed the heads off. It didn't feel right but my friends were screaming with excitement. As we ran around the city, we felt exuberant. Passing a bookshop, Jung led everyone inside. He began to go through the shelves and threw revisionist books into the street. Su Bin struck a match and soon a bonfire lit up the night sky.

I noticed a large book that was taking longer to burn. I prodded it with a stick and I saw blackened sheets of thick creamy paper printed with Daoist landscapes. Its nine shades of black had become a single darkness. I felt sick, made excuses and turned for home feeling a deep sense of shame. We were just doing what our great leaders wanted so why did I feel sick? Why couldn't I do it? What was wrong with me? It was like the time I couldn't kill the sparrows but this was different. Then my friends had joked with me but now some of the boys looked scary when I broke away: they thought I must be a coward.

On my way to school the next morning for revolutionary activities, I met Weiwei in the street. I hadn't seen him for ages. Weiwei asked me if my father was still working from the Summer Palace. My look of dismay answered him but I asked, 'What about your father?'

'My father is denounced as a Capitalist Roader ... I don't understand it. There must be some mistake. He fought the Japanese, he fought the Kuomintang and helped build factories all over Northern China. He's a good revolutionary.'

'Oh Weiwei I ...' but then I stopped. My father had been going out in the morning but coming back looking haggard and defeated. I thought he was ill and asked Mother if I could get him anything or give his feet a massage.

'Weiwei, could my father be accused as well?'

'It sounds like it. Have you heard about what happened at Chairman Mao's daughter's school?' It seemed that I knew nothing.

'I don't understand it. How is it Chairman Mao is not flaming angry? Why doesn't he condemn it?' continued Weiwei, assuming I already knew.

'Condemn what?'

'The girls attacked their headmistress. They kicked her and walked over her and then poured boiling water over her.'

I couldn't believe what I was hearing.

'Is she all right?'

'No. She is dead. They ordered her to carry heavy bricks. When she stumbled, they whipped her with the buckle end of army belts until she collapsed and died.'

'How do you know all this?'

'Chairman Mao praised the girl who led the attack. Don't you remember during the rally in The Square? He invited her to come on the stage and asked her name. She said "Son Binbin".'

'I remember. He asked the crowd, "Is it the Bin as in educated and gentle?" And she nodded.'

I hadn't seen Weiwei looking so agitated before as he said,

'Have you forgotten that Chairman Mao told her to be violent? So she has changed her name to "Be Violent."'

'You must have misheard it, Weiwei. Chairman Mao wouldn't have approved.' I should have listened more carefully. My mind was filled with the picture of him framed by sunlight. My eye remembers imagery more than words. Still, I would hear no criticism of Chairman Mao and was about to turn away in a huff, when I had a thought.

'Has it something to do with his wife and the others?'

'Maybe, Little Winter, maybe but have you seen the latest posters? "Stuff human feelings. We will be brutal. We will strike you (Mao's enemies) to the ground and trample you."'

That night, I wanted to talk to my parents about what Weiwei had said but my father returned, ashen-faced, murmuring the name Lao She. I knew Lao She was China's most famous writer and he wrote plays as well as poems and novels. My parents enjoyed the theatre and I loved listening to mother describing the Chekhov plays she had watched in Moscow, in 1950, when she was there for a while, improving her Russian and making links with the University. Daddy said,

'Lao She is dead', and went into their bedroom and slammed the door. I asked my mother what had happened.

'Some Red Guards paraded Lao She before crowds and beat him with belts. When he managed to get home, his wife would not let him in – Lao She died in Taiping Lake.'

The next day I understood. When I arrived at school, it was already crowded but I didn't recognise the students. When I saw our Son Bin, for a moment, I shivered remembering the story Weiwei had told me. But his story couldn't be true – just a nasty rumour.

She smiled at me and I relaxed thinking our Son Bin is kind, not like the one in Weiwei's imagination. She waved to me and then indicated the seated groups who were older than us. They looked more like sixteen or seventeen.

'They have come from Hebei to learn how to be revolutionaries.'

Surely they wanted to see the giant posters all over our school? Would they admire the ones I'd worked on? But they stayed seated on the ground where we practised Phys Ed – when we learned Phys Ed – before we became revolutionaries. Everyone seemed excited and expectant. It was a hot, dry day and the crowd made it seem even hotter. I wished I had brought the cream fan my mother had given me at Chinese New Year.

My thoughts were trampled as a platoon of Red Guards from the High School marched in, leading our headmistress onto the stage. The two standing behind her stepped forward and grabbed her roughly under her arms. Forcing her head down, while holding her body up, they made her kow-tow to us. The 'audience' from Hebei started to boo. I looked around anxiously at my classmates – they were quiet. As the noise grew louder, two Red Guards marched forward, head held high and took off their military leather belts with heavy metal buckles. I saw the brass glint in the sunlight as they began to beat her. Remembering what Weiwei had told me, I wanted to cry out, 'Stop it, stop it,' but I didn't; I just sat there saying nothing.

I watched as she collapsed and fell over, and they pulled her up by her hair and started all over again. How could they do that? I wanted to shout, 'STOP', but I bit my lips and remained silent. I was afraid because the crowd was going crazy with frenzied cheering. By then, even some of the girls from our school joined in the abuse. I felt ashamed. As the fury abated it was followed by an eerie silence and a sense of relief swept over me. As soon as I could get out of there, I rushed to my only refuge, my home.

Sara, you would think it tiny but by the standards of Beijing, in 1966, we were privileged to have three rooms. Imagine how upset I was when I arrived home to learn that we would probably have to move.

Grandmother had died a few months earlier. My parents explained we must leave the flat and live in a one-roomed apartment. MaMa said,

'Now that NaiNai has died, we must give it up for a bigger family.'

'Couldn't we invite someone to share this flat rather than move?'

She didn't answer me. An ugly noise interrupted us; I ran to the window. Below, a crowd of Red Guards had formed a circle and in the middle stood a terrified girl I thought I recognised. They were cutting off her long hair roughly, like poor Mimi, leaving her in tears of humiliation. Then they started criticising her clothes and one boy pushed her saying,

'You capitalist slut! We shall teach you a lesson.'

And he used his scissors to slash the skirt she was wearing. A strange excited look spread over his face. His hand went to his crotch as if it hurt him. I had a skirt like that. That could be me! Mother saw it too and bought us all new clothes: for herself, for me and for dad all the same blue military style uniform. From now on everyone dressed alike whatever their age or sex. The only choice was whether to wear grey or blue, old or new, unless you were in the armed forces. I looked admiringly at mother; her delicate features were not remotely overwhelmed by the shapeless clothes.

October 1966: My first taste of exile

A few nights later, we sat around our lacquered dining table. My mother put a pot of chrysanthemum tea on the table and as she began to pour it into our small straight-sided porcelain cups, my father held out his hand.

'Xiaodong, we think you should leave Beijing for a while and come back when things have calmed down. I have written to Uncle Chang and he will look after you.'

I had never travelled anywhere on my own before. Uncle Chang was a farmer. I think my parents had taken me to visit his family when I was little but the only thing I remembered was how black the night was. I didn't want to go.

Carrying my quilt on my back, I set off alone. The three hours on the train to Yixian felt like six. Uncle was there to meet me but there was still another fifteen kilometres to go to Shi Zhuan Commune. That does not seem far but he only had a bike. He loaded my luggage on the front and back and pushed it. I was exhausted and afraid for MaMa and BaBa. Ever since the death of Lao She, they seemed to be suspended in a fearful mood, expecting something to happen.

Uncle was a man of few words and I felt anxious and shy, so the journey passed in silence. When we eventually arrived at the village it was in complete darkness, as I had remembered it. It had no lights because it had no electricity. Inside, the house was lit by an oil lamp and my aunt showed me to a bed covered by an unfamiliar mosquito net. The floor beneath was made from mud brick. The roof was made of loose thatch and I imagined creepy crawlies dropping on me while I slept. Although auntie was kind and sympathetic, I couldn't settle. All I could think about was what was happening at home. Would my parents have left our flat? Were they safe from Red Guard attacks? The loneliness and anxiety was so hard that I cried every day.

The first month passed slowly but without event. I helped in the house and the fields and no questions were asked and there was no conversation but I became more attached to the landscape. Towards sunset, I asked Auntie if I could go and sketch the fields glowing crimson with the sorghum ready for harvesting. She couldn't think of a reason to say no.

I strode through the fields and sat down near a neighbouring village to colour my paper red, when I was struck by the sound of a crowd shouting wildly. The commotion seemed to be coming from the village cemetery, which in China, is situated near the boundary and not in the heart of a village. I followed the sound and turning a corner by a mud brick wall to the south of the village I discovered the cause. The fist-waving crowd was looking towards the solitary tree in the graveyard. It was gnarled but beautiful, the type which often grace Chinese paintings.

The man hanging from the tree was a landlord. I immediately knew his designation because, in the countryside, landlords were forced to dress in black and a white label was sewn on his back, marking his crime of owning property.

Sara, you have been taught about Jewish people in Nazi Germany being forced to wear the Star of David. The ostracism and abuse this labelled man had experienced led him to take his own life and the villagers stood in a semi-circle taunting and jeering at his dead body.

Shaken, I edged away from the harrowing scene and made my way towards the centre of the village. I heard more shouting coming from a narrow street. A young man, sweat pouring down his reddened face, was crying and screaming. He stumbled and fell writhing with desperate sounds pouring from him.

He was trying to save himself and his wife and children. He was denouncing his father, for he was the son of the dead man. He yelled at the crowd around him,

'My father has nothing to do with me; he was a counter-revolutionary.

He was against the people, but I am for the people. He deserved it. He deserved to die for his crimes.'

Seeing people twisted like the branches of that tree, joyful at the death of a fellow human, I ran back into the crimson field and was violently sick.

January 1967: Back-packing around China

The next day Uncle Chang put me on the train home. I'm not sure what I was expecting but my relief at finding both of my parents still living in the only home I'd known lit up my face. The bleak tension of not knowing ebbed away and they seemed pleased to have me back. The problem was that there was nothing I could focus on. Competitive skating was no longer regarded as socialist but had been labelled 'capitalist' and was abolished. Schools no longer functioned with normal lessons. There was nothing I could do unless I became a Red Guard. But even that, I couldn't do. My mother had been criticised and that disqualified me. As far as Red Guards were concerned, I was taboo. How could I spend the time? Only sketching and practicing calligraphy gave me any satisfaction.

A few days later Jia called to see me and asked if I would travel with her. She wanted to see where Mao had his headquarters during the wars. 'Everyone is doing it, Jie Jie. We can travel without paying a Yuan – you will come, won't you?'

That evening, I asked MaMa. 'You are too young to be travelling alone, Xiaodong.'

I wasn't yet fifteen. I felt so disappointed. Jia came to my rescue saying,

'But she won't be alone. I'll be with her and I *am* fifteen and I promise I'll look after her.' Mother reluctantly agreed and gave me some money but said I must try to phone them; we were unusual in having a phone at home. So in mid–October we set off backpacking. It felt different from going to uncle's village because Jia was such good company.

Mao's troops had entered Yenan (Shanxi) in 1937, after the Long March, and it became his home for a decade. That was why it seemed, to Jia, the obvious place to head for inspiration, the number one pilgrimage destination! We got as far as Tong Chuan by rail, changing trains at Xian on the way. Arriving at the terminus, we were surprised to discover that we were not the only teenage travellers heading for Mao's old headquarters. The whole world seemed to be heading there! We joined a vast queue waiting, in the cold drizzle, for a lorry and it was late evening before we climbed on ours.

We were as ravenous as only teenagers can be and the local people provided all the young travellers with food. As I waited in line, I grew hungrier and hungrier until finally I reached the front of the queue. I watched as the woman put a ladle of broad noodles flavoured with chilli, salt and spring onions into a bowl. She then took half a spoonful of boiling oil and poured it over the noodles: we called this dish oil-splashed noodles. I grinned at Jia and she grinned back. I thought it the most delicious meal I had tasted since my mother's egg fried rice with bamboo shoots during the famine years. But the oil-splashed noodles didn't satisfy me for long. The lorry twisted and turned along a pot-holed road. My stomach heaved as it wound up the dramatic hills and then swung back down into the steep sided valleys; the nausea didn't end until we arrived in Yenan the next afternoon.

Jia and I emerged tired but excited. Once again the local people turned out and fed us – this time with pumpkin soup – as yellow as the landscape around us. The sun made gold the nine-storey, thousand-year-old pagoda but we were not Buddhist pilgrims: our aim was to see the house Mao had called home.

Sara, now I feel deeply shocked and ashamed that I helped vandalise the temple, chopping off Buddha heads in the niches. My only explanation for my behaviour is that our minds were filled with other things, our holy places were where Chairman Mao had walked, lived or swam.

My heart raced as I stepped over the threshold of his house. I was filled with awe as I gently sat on his chair and caressed his desk. It was like a religious experience. Captivated, I surprised myself by hugging Jia and saying,

'Let's follow the revolutionary road forever!'

Not long after we left, the attendant put a string across the chair to prevent anyone else sitting on it since the cane seat was already frayed. I proudly wrote home explaining I had sat on the very chair where Chairman Mao had written his thoughts and will probably be the last person to do so. I couldn't believe my good fortune. Jia and I had no idea where to go next but had lost our anxiety and fell in love instead with the adventure.

'Jie Jie, lets head for the sun!' suggested my friend who was becoming like a sister to me.

Jie Jie is usually an affectionate name for sister, Sara.

The trains heading south were packed and noisy. Some students climbed on the roofs of the carriages preferring that to the smelly insides and revolting toilets. In each town where we stopped there was a welcome organisation to meet us and accommodation was either free or very cheap. The students organised meetings with local people to preach revolution to them. In Xian, fighting broke out when the crowds split into factions.

Jia grabbed my arm and I pulled her away from the noisy crowd.

'I need a swim, Jie Jie. Let's find a pool' and in the depths of the blue water, we found serenity.

It took a few days but we eventually arrived in Shanghai, on the way seeing some of China's most picturesque places for the first time. Shanghai seemed like another country when we left the narrow alleys for the old French quarter. Jia got very bored when I stopped to sketch some architectural details. She, unusually for 1967, owned a camera.

'At this rate we'll never see more than a couple of regions. Why don't I take photographs and you sketch from them when we get home?'

I knew what I wanted so snapped two pictures of Jia, right arm outstretched in Red Guard pose.

'Go easy, Chowy, film's expensive. I save on the developing. Weiwei does it for me. You hear stories of brothers and sisters informing on each other. I must be lucky. Weiwei's a great brother – well most of the time.'

She giggled knowingly at me and said, 'But when he hides my things; then I feel like telling on him!'

Laughing, we headed for a noodle shop and set off in the direction of the Huangpu River. The atmosphere was hot and sticky, and all the walking was exhausting so not only our revolutionary fervour but that of other revolutionary travellers seemed to slow and become less intense. I felt embarrassed when a boy looked at me in a strange, intimate way. Shocked, I grabbed Jia's hand and dragged her into a shop and bought a book called *The Daughter of the Army* that described a young woman's life in a construction team in the New Territories in the west where China meets Turkmenistan. Jia was excited by it and suggested we head west.

'What is to stop us joining a worker's brigade? What do you think, Chowy?'

'Let's do it ... what are we waiting for?'

So Sara, I had spent my fifteenth birthday not in wintery Beijing but in steaming Shanghai enjoying a sunny day like you had for your fifteenth birthday party, last week. You will find it hard to believe but despite travelling all over China with boys, I was completely naïve as were most of my friends; we knew nothing about sex.

Neither our parents nor teachers had uttered a word of warning. We felt free and liberated but it was not the kind of liberation that was breaking out in the West in the sixties. I wanted to believe that the upheaval – all the frightening things I had seen – was about freedom for the young. I hoped with all my heart that Chairman Mao would hear about the excesses and put a stop to them. And then ... then the young could enjoy an exciting future.

Our journey west proved harder than the others. The trains were snail trains. During the day we sweated in the sweltering heat but at night the temperatures would sink below zero. Sometimes the boredom was relieved by the sight of animals or birds. One day a flight of graceful swallows swept over train and off into the distant horizon.

Jia said, 'I wish we could fly. They seem so free and they are really beautiful.'

I told you that Jia's name meant beautiful, and in my eyes she was beautiful, but she sometimes described herself as a dumpling. On this day she said, ' I wish I could change my name; I'd love to be called Fei Yen. Fei (Fay) Yen means flying swallows.' From then on, I'd sometimes call her Fei.

Anyway, we made it as far as the capital Uru Muqi. The people of the state were mostly Uighurs of Muslim background, not Han Chinese like Jia and I, so we felt like explorers.

Our romantic illusions were shattered in Uru Muqi. Instead of the unutterable beauty we had visualised reading The Daughter of the Army, before us was dreadful squalor, disease, beggars and hunger. It was a dangerous place because the revolutionary groups used guns instead of fists to fight each other. It is difficult to describe just how inhospitable the landscape was beyond the city. As far as the naked eye could see lay a mirror of thick ice reflecting the clouds. But I stopped looking at it with any pleasure as we slipped and skidded as the temperatures plummeted to minus twenty. We saw Red Guards using only water on the back of their posters to hang them up because as soon as they were placed on the wall, they froze in position! Our clothes could not keep us warm and our shoes were of no use on this ice rink for there were no paved roads. Jia and I hugged each other for warmth. The gloss of being revolutionary travellers had worn away.

I opened my mouth to say, 'I want to go home' but nothing came out. I didn't want to admit that I ached for home. I looked at Jia. We needed no words. We turned around and the journey back was easier than the outward trip because Prime Minister Zhou Enlai, like us, wanted the revolutionary travelling to stop. All young people were ordered back to their homes and the railways were instructed to help us. So we returned, as ordered, our self-respect intact thanks to Zhou!

But when I reached home it was not the one I had left. Soon after the rally in Tiananmen Square the previous August, Liu Shaoqi and Deng Xiaoping were found guilty, and the suffering of Liu and his wife Wang Guangmei began in earnest. They were subjected to the most brutal treatment before being separated and put in solitary confinement where Liu died a painful and lingering death.

Jia's mother and my mother taught in the University and while we were travelling their lives had turned into a nightmare. By April 1967, the revolutionary fervour in the University had intensified and posters appeared denouncing individual teachers. Jia's mother telephoned MaMa to warn her that she had seen one with her name on it, and offered to help hide her. The poster accused my Russian-speaking mother of being a Chinese Khrushchev.

Before my mother had put the receiver down, a sudden noise came from the corridor and the door to her office swung open so violently it almost fell from its hinges. She turned to greet her uninvited guests. They kicked and beat her, and then when her normally immaculate appearance was sufficiently damaged, prepared to drag her through the streets. Once outside they pulled her onto a platform to be jeered at by thousands of young people, just as my head teacher had been jeered. They raised a cheer when the Black Cap was forcefully thrust on the head; the cap was lined with sharp nails. They forced her onto her knees and pulled her arms back in the painful Jet position. She was their 'legitimate' target because anyone who had worked with Liu Shaoqi was a member of The Black Gang. The label the Red Guards hung around her neck read 'Capitalist Roader'.

When they had finished with her, they sent her to a labour camp in the neighbouring province of Hebei. I was spared knowing the details at that time: my awareness grew as I witnessed what happened to others labelled 'Capitalist Roader'. Jia's mother had watched it from her office. She must have been afraid that she would be the next to wear the black cap. She hid any anxiety she felt from me. She simply said,

'Bo Lin has been criticized. She has been sent to the countryside for re-education. Your mother is brave and strong – she will come back, Xiaodong.'

I ran home desperate to see my father but arrived to find an empty house.

I hurried to the engineering department where he worked but stopped short a hundred yards away. I saw him from a distance being kicked from behind by a crowd of Red Guards. He looked like a broken man. I didn't want him to know I had seen him. He would not have been able to look at me in the same loving way he had before if he knew I had seen him humiliated. He would feel diminished. So I headed home and bought some vegetables and prepared a meal for him. When he came through the door, he smelt different. Then I realised what the smell was. They had made my brilliant father empty the latrines.

He washed and tried to eat. At first he didn't say anything but then he hugged me and said, 'I missed my little girl'.

'I miss Ma. Will she be all right?'

'Your mother was attacked because she supported Liu and Deng. As long as Deng is out of favour with Chairman Mao, her life will be difficult. She may not look it but she's strong. She was in the PLA – she knew hard times: harder than you can imagine, Xiaodong.' He paused and lowered his head, remembering something, before looking straight at me and saying firmly.

'She will survive. But you must be careful, my daughter. Remember: listen but don't talk. Keep this in your mind at all times: illness comes in through the mouth but disaster comes out through the mouth.'

Weiwei

Sara, I did try to listen and heed my father's advice. I know you try to listen to me, Sara, when I talk about drugs and sex but sometimes you hear but don't really listen. Life is constantly changing and you don't think I understand your world. So how do I get you to understand the world as I knew it at your age?

Every day was filled with the unexpected. The fifth of April is the day of the tomb-sweeping festival when we show respect to our ancestors. On that day, as I cycled near to the Eight Treasures Mountain Revolutionary Cemetery, I was sure it would be honoured.

In Chinese art, mountains are more than places to climb; shrouded in the mists of the Dao they define the soul and so this was a fitting place to honour our revolutionary heroes. I sat and sketched but my mind drifted away from the heroes and I saw only the landscape. I can't remember how long I stayed there but when I finished, my pictures had a quality, a yearning beauty and a purity like wu wei, which flowed from within. Yet none of them included people. I rolled them up and began walking back down the hill when I saw Weiwei, Jia's brother. I waved to him and he smiled, looking pleased to see me. The warm spring sun lit up our faces as we followed the crowds heading towards the Summer Palace. Of course, it was no longer our weekend home now that our parents were Capitalist Roaders. We parked our bikes near to the Eastern Palace Gate. Crowds were milling near the entrance. The sound of angry disputes and haranguing ugly words shattered my illusions. The latest self-appointed cadres of Red Guards were denouncing writers and artists. I didn't mean to say anything but it just came out:

'But artists are the eyes that see into the soul.'

They came towards me and saw the scroll in my hand; a sneering Red Guard grabbed it. When he unrolled it, his face filled with contempt and he pushed me angrily and called me names.

'This is capitalist art. You are a disgrace, an enemy of the revolution and need teaching a lesson.'

He tore up my pictures and began to hit me. Weiwei pushed me aside and hit the Red Guard. Then a group of them grabbed him so he couldn't move. I think one blow knocked him out and they threw him in the back of a lorry and drove away. At first I stood there, looking helplessly down the road as the cloud of dust whipped up by the lorry disappeared into the distance. But then I cycled as fast as I could to Weiwei's home and told his parents what had happened. I felt so ashamed. Why hadn't I listened to my father? I began to cry. Weiwei's mother looked distraught – and angry. But his father looked hard at her then turned to me.

'You know why you, Weiwei and Jia can't be Red Guards? It is because of us – because they call us Capitalist Roaders. That is why you must be careful. You stand out. You don't have the uniform. What direction did the lorry go in? I will try to find my son before they send me away.'

I had so much I wanted to say – I felt – I didn't really know how to say it but at that moment I knew I cared more for Weiwei than anyone else in the world. I was uncomfortable because I knew the Chairman and my parents must be first in my life.

I told my father what had happened and he helped me.

'Weiwei is a real man. Be proud of him. Don't listen to those who condemn him. He will come back.'

And he did. Two days later. He had been released but looked dreadful. He would rather I didn't see him just yet, not until the bruises had faded a bit. Jia told me all and added, 'Don't worry. He is all right. He will be all right. They took him to the Sports School where you trained. They interrogated him and tried to beat the answers out of him – the ones they wanted to hear - but he didn't give them the pleasure. I think my brother is great.'

'I think your brother is great too.' Jia could see how I felt. She smiled. She didn't seem to mind sharing him. 'I think his sister is great too.' Jia looked uncomfortable but leaned towards me and said,

'He says he has an idea, and the three of us and some friends we can trust should get together next week.'

Angering Madame Mao

Red Guards were not all the same. The first Red Guards thought they were extending the revolution their parents had begun and most were from backgrounds like mine and Weiwei's. Once the Gang of Four got to work, new cadres formed and attacked them as revisionists. Really Sara, they were puppets manipulated by the Gang.

The Gang of Four told the latest Red Guards when raiding houses to hold on to anything particularly poisonous and not destroy it but take it to them as evidence. They amassed wonderful collections of antiques. But really they wanted to use these young revolutionaries to overturn any party official who admired the Prime Minister, Zhou Enlai or the now disgraced Deng Xiaoping and Liu Shaoqi. It was all about power; they wanted absolute power. But this was all hidden, or at least not spoken about.

The following week, we met in Beihai Park. There were ten of us in all. Weiwei's bruises were still evident but I was relieved to see that he was still handsome. I had worried that they would have made him ugly. I smiled a shy smile. We were all eager to know what he wanted to tell us.

'We are here because all our parents have been called Capitalist Roaders and we know they have done nothing wrong. We have seen our teachers beaten and know that is wrong. Why is this all happening?'

We all wanted an answer but could not think of one. Weiwei answered for us;

'I don't think Chairman Mao's aware of what is happening. He's surrounded by people who don't want him to know.'

We all knew who he meant – The Gang of Four.

'There is nothing to stop us forming our own group of Red Guards. People are doing it all the time.' We looked at each other surprised. 'I propose we speak the truth. We need a symbol of truth. That will be your job, Little Winter. We must make posters denouncing the attacks on teachers.'

A few looked nervous but we all wanted to do it and were all given different tasks. Symbol of truth? Now that needed some thought. I walked and walked as I tried to think. But nothing ...

Passing the Forbidden City, I decided to go inside and see if it could inspire me. The Forbidden City is huge and impressive. I walked from pavilion to pavilion. It felt strangely peaceful, almost another world. Dragons of course were everywhere. What about a dragon? Or a crane? Cranes were elegant. Something abstract perhaps, the ancient swastika, the wheel? Tired, I sat in the Qianlong garden and took out my pencil and paper. Then I looked at what I was drawing. Rocks. It was suddenly obvious what I had to do. Rocks are at the heart of any Chinese garden, they outlive everything else, they are solid unchangeable – the truth.

I drew an outline so the rock seemed most solid at the bottom but pointed upwards leaving plenty of space for calligraphy inside. When I was satisfied, I ran to Weiwei's home. Their flat was almost identical to ours but less furnished and tidier. There always seemed to be piles of newspapers and journals on our table and I didn't always clear away my ink set. I placed my design on the bare black table and I could see immediately that he was impressed. He smiled and leant towards me. My hand trembled as I smoothed the edge of the paper. Weiwei leant towards me; his lips hovered near mine but then he drew back and shook my hand.

Our revolutionary group met again the following day in the park by the willows dipping their fingers in the water like the traditional picture on porcelain that my NaiNai used to like. The team working on the words came up with their suggestions. Because I am a good calligrapher, they asked me to try out a few and see how they looked. After much discussion, we chose:

Stand up for truth and harmony.
Support the people against the despots.
Tell Chairman Mao the truth.

It took a few days to make twenty posters. We intended to print them but thought that could be risky so in the end we made each one by hand. On the

Friday night, we went in pairs intending to put up four each. Jia and I headed towards Beijing University. Finding places to put them was not easy. I pasted the first one on a wall next to a huge poster of a smiling Chairman Mao which read:

The sunlight of Mao Zedong thought illuminates the road of the great proletarian Cultural Revolution.

It reminded me of that wonderful day in Tiananmen Square when he had beamed at me. Jia read my thoughts. She pointed to another around the corner by a noodle shop. This one read,

Criticize the old world and build a new world with Mao Zedong Thought as a weapon.

Just what Lin Biao had asked us to do. So we pasted ours beside it. We turned back and went into the campus heading towards the pagoda. The featureless modern buildings we passed on the way were festooned with posters. One disturbed me; like a nightmare I wanted to forget.

Hold high the great red banner of Mao Zedong Thought: smash the rotting counter-revolutionary revisionist line in literature and art.

I pictured Weiwei's bruises, all because I had spoken up for artists and writers. I pasted our last poster on top of that one splashing on the brush as if I was beating the hell out of his tormenters. It felt great. We all felt great.

The next day, I walked around the University area where Jia and I had pasted our posters. I couldn't believe it; the whole area was a collage of posters but ours, only ours, had disappeared. Who had taken them? Someone was talking excitedly about Madame Mao. I tried to look uninterested but moved closer and heard enough to believe that they had been delivered to her.

The group had arranged to meet at our usual destination in the afternoon. Everyone looked worried; all twenty posters had been taken down. Our hopes of stimulating discussion were dashed. We should have recognised the danger when we saw how frightened Yi looked. He was there when the posters were taken down and talked of Madame Mao's anger. He shook as he told us that she had ordered an investigation into who had put up our posters.

On Sunday afternoon, I called for Jia. She looked anxious and afraid. 'Weiwei is missing, we don't know where he is.'

My whole body went taut and my stomach knotted but I knew I must try to think clearly.

'Leave it to me. I'll find him.'

I had made a rash promise because I wasn't sure what to do. I thought I would ask father but as I cycled home, an idea came to me. I sought out Liu Wang and Yao Zisheng, my old friends from the Skating School. I reminded them what good actors they were. Could you pretend to be outraged when you heard about the posters and find out what had happened to Weiwei?

'Stop crying, and go home Chowy – we'll come as soon as we have anything to report.'

They were as good as their word. I let them in but left the door open so the neighbours would not be suspicious. I made tea in our little brown terracotta pot and pushed all the paints and papers to one side. I placed the cups and teapot on the uncovered area of our rust red table. We sat on the dark lacquered chairs and I glanced over my shoulder to see if anyone was eavesdropping. By now I felt you could trust no one but here were these friends trusting me.

'It didn't take long.' Wang said looking directly at me. 'As soon as we showed enthusiasm for The Gang's latest campaign, they were only too eager to tell us. We're sorry but Yi has informed on Weiwei.'

'Yi! How could he?'

'Fear. He hoped to save himself and maybe the rest of you by saying it was Weiwei's idea. Weiwei has been arrested as the ring leader and charged with being counter-revolutionary,' said Liu.

'And taken to Beijing Number 2 Prison,' said Yao.

At that time the most serious crime was to be counter-revolutionary: every day we heard stories of executions. The situation was now so volatile that someone could be accused one day and become a hero the next. We heard about one poor man who accidentally used a torn off piece of newspaper to wipe his bottom. That scrap had a photo of Mao on it, so he was sentenced to death for dishonouring the revolution. True or not, we all believed it. That night, I cried myself to sleep. In the morning, I told my father about Weiwei's arrest. He shouted,

'Fuck them ... fuck the bastards.'

I put my fingers to my lips and whispered,

'The walls have ears.'

'You are growing wise, Xiaodong.'

'Ba, I miss MaMa. Is there any way I can get to see her?'

'If she has received our letters, Xiaodong, she hasn't been allowed to reply.

Try not to worry; things may change. There is a rumour that Chairman Mao is getting fed up with the chaos. Children are running the schools. The army is running the hospitals and making the surgeons work as porters when they don't want them to operate on one of them! The factories are chaotic; the workers' time is spent in factional fighting. Even on the farms, there is politics and more politics. Unless something is done to stop the anarchy, there will be famine.'

He put out his hand and covered mine, saying,

'Weiwei may be safer in prison. On the streets he could easily be killed for criticising Madame Mao. But our prisons are cold, hard places. At this moment he will be sitting on a concrete floor. Make him some padded clothes and see if you and his father can deliver them.'

'Ba, I will. I'll start right away.'

I told Professor and Mrs Hu, WeiWei and Jia's parents, what my father had suggested and they thought it a good idea. So a few days later, Professor Hu, Jia and I set off with a parcel of warm clothes and books. We were careful to select approved books but hopefully included paper and pencils.

We boarded the number 15 bus, which in just three stops arrived at Beijing Zoo. We changed there for the number 27. At our destination, we needed to ask an old man the way to the prison because we had never been to this district before. There wasn't such a thing as a street map of Beijing to help us. He pointed the way. Weiwei's father's mouth was tightly closed and his fists clenched. It was a dank and gloomy afternoon. We didn't speak a word as we hurried down the road ahead. Turning a corner we came to a sudden halt; looming over us was a twenty to thirty meter high wall with electric wires on the top. As we approached the prison, the shadow of those immense walls shrouded us in darkness. Professor Hu marched up to the forbidding dark red gate. There was a tiny peep-hole through which he addressed the warden. A cold hard voice impatiently commanded us.

'What do you want?'

We identified ourselves and Weiwei's father said he was convinced that his son was in the prison and we had come to see him, bringing necessary things.

'Wait' said the disembodied voice. I could see only his eyes. 'Stand far away, not near the gate.'

We looked around and saw lying by the road, part of an old millstone. We sat on it, and Professor Hu took a deep breath low in his stomach, clenched his fists and then relaxed them. Then he looked up, eyes stretched wide as he stared at the closed gate. We waited and waited as passers-by came and went, most glancing at us sympathetically. In all that time the Prof hardly moved and didn't speak. He seemed as solid as a sculpture but I could penetrate that hard surface and read his thoughts. After all the suffering and struggle to make the revolution, he couldn't believe this outcome. He couldn't have foreseen himself sitting here outside a prison in which his son was incarcerated.

It felt like hours before a little window opened and a voice told us to approach. Then we noticed that there was a small door within the huge gate. It opened. It was just large enough for one person to pass through. The warden said we could leave the things for him but we couldn't see Weiwei. I was surprised when his father insisted he send a receipt; that way we would know for definite that he had received the parcel. He then handed it over and the door banged shut. We were relieved. He was alive.

But Father's vision of an end to the chaos was not in sight. 'Revolutionary' groups were fighting each other day and night and I longed for escape. Wanting something, anything to take our mind off all our unhappiness and anxiety, I suggested that I take Jia to the zoo.

Taking Jia's hand, I led her to the tiger's cage, longing to see the tiger's piercing mysterious eyes. He was pacing up and down restlessly disturbed by the raucous sounds of slogans and insults that echoed from the nearby streets. Jia read my disappointment at the eerie and abandoned atmosphere. Despondent we headed home. I said goodbye to Jia, turned the corner and faced a welcoming party. Four boys surrounded me.

'You are Xiaodong? We are from the People's Dictatorship Office and you are wanted for questioning.'

There was no point denying my name. Everyone around knew me and plenty would want the honour of showing how revolutionary they were by searching out enemies.

Sara, nobody knew who organized a People's Dictatorship Office or where it was registered. Nobody knew how many people had died, for no good cause on the orders of those dictatorships. But my connection to Weiwei had been noticed and I had been summoned to The People's Dictatorship Office in our district. In that one year, I had been battered emotionally. I had learned excitement, hysteria and horror and now, I was about to discover fear.

It was a lead grey afternoon when I arrived at the small room not far from my school playground. I opened the door into a narrow room with solid walls on three sides and one tiny window on the wall where the door was. One 25 watt light bulb suspended from the ceiling in the middle of the room hardly penetrated the gloom. A desk and three chairs were situated below the pale attempt at light. On one wall, painted in bold brush strokes, were eight Chinese characters:

Lenience for confession and severe punishment for defiance.

My critical faculties distracted me; I was annoyed that the calligraphy was badly written! Why did I notice that when I needed to focus on oppressive things not calligraphy? But now I believe it helped because my mind was calm when I took in the rest of the room.

The opposite wall was hung with ropes, iron chains and baseball bats. I became nervous as I felt something wet under foot but stopped myself from looking down. There was no way out and I told myself to stay calm and strong, and to see what they wanted.

I looked at the three people sat behind the desk. I did not know the name of the one sitting in the middle because he was not from around Millionaires' Village Avenue. He was pale with a pair of hard eyes and tight thin lips that he wetted constantly with the tip of his tongue. Next to him was our Son Bin, a school pal. The third, a boy with a solemn face, dropped his eyes at the first sight of me; it was Yi. I knew he was trying to avoid the awkwardness of greetings and so I consciously kept silent.

'Sit down', said Thin Lips as he signalled to a wobbly stool. From that position, I had to look up at him. The way Thin Lips looked at me unsettled me. It was more leer than official appraisal. He got up and walked behind me. He fingered my Mao tunic at the back as if checking to see it was made from the correct material. His fingers moved on my flesh. I felt disgustingly dirty. It was not just my opinions that were under scrutiny. Squatting on the stool beneath him, he turned me into more of an object than a person.

The lasting silence seemed intentional, to make me nervous and afraid. I focused on my breathing, taking slow deep breaths, and waited.

'Do you know why we asked you to come here?' Thin Lips demanded.

'I don't know.' I tried to regulate the sound of my voice to appear friendly.

Silence and more silence. The dagger eye turned to Yi who raised his, gave me a quick glance, then dropped them immediately before saying in a rather placid manner:

'We ... have acquired some information, concerning your conduct ... you know our policy,' he said, casting a look at the Chinese characters on the wall.

I nodded and he continued:

'You know, we have never wronged any good person, nor have we let any bad person escape ...'

Thin Lips interrupted in a staccato voice,

'Look at this,' unrolling one of the rock posters. 'Tell me. Did you make this?'

With Yi sitting opposite, I could hardly deny it.

'Are you criticising Comrade Jiang Qing and the Cultural Revolution?' said Son Bin. Her fervent, shining eyes pierced mine. I felt my brain seize. To criticise Madame Mao – she who embodied the Cultural Revolution – could be a death crime so I responded immediately, without hesitation.

'Who has spread this rumour? It is total nonsense! I have never been opposed to Comrade Jiang Qing! Whoever says that is a liar!' I lied.

'Don't get too worked up. You had better tell us the truth!' snapped Thin Lips.

'That's what the poster was about – the truth.'

Possibly my answer worked here and they fell into silence too.

Then Son Bin said, 'You have to be responsible for what you say'.

'Of course,' I said firmly.

I made a written statement and signed it. Thin Lips leaned slowly forward and looked me over as if examining every inch of me, every nook and cranny and then, his threatening gaze fell full on my face, but his words gave me temporary relief.

'You can leave for now. We will all think about you and what you have done. Perhaps there are ways that your behaviour could change that makes it more attractive to the People's Dictatorship Committee. We will talk to you again.'

I didn't expect the enquiry to end so quickly. Once out of the room, my chest turn to wood and my heart banged against it, wanting to take flight. How easy it had been to lie as I denied the times I had expressed my opposition to Madame Mao. For the moment, I had got away with it because our 'big-character' posters were deliberately ambiguous, but they were critical of the violent attacks on teachers that were at the heart of the Cultural Revolution. Yi had gone over to the other side but maybe he was protecting me, his old friend. After all, they hadn't even beaten me. I was too young and naïve then to even consider that Thin Lips protected me for a possible future encounter.

I made my way to the swimming pool to wash away the feelings of oppression. After the claustrophobia of that room, I felt my body glide smoothly through the water. I could imagine myself floating above the darkness below. My strokes grew stronger until the exercise freed my mind. After my swim, I went to see Jia, worried in case she had been sent for too. But no, she was fine and her cheerful personality lifted my spirits even more as we walked side by side towards my home. Our new world was unpredictable. Who knew what would happen tomorrow and who would be put into positions of power over us? Thin Lips could only have been a couple of years older than me yet he was drunk on his new self-importance. In a different time and in a different place, he would have been nothing. That was the great lesson I took from the interrogation by the People's Dictatorship Committee.

Red Women's Army on Ice

Sara, recently the Olympics took place in Beijing and the world's finest athletes competed in stadiums on which no expense was spared. Think of me at your age hoping to compete with the finest. You complain that I am a tiger mother driving you too hard to achieve. If you understand my disappointments, then maybe you'll see how I want the best for you.

I had the ambition to qualify for the national skating team when competitive sport ended - just like that, within a week. And it was awfully hard to adjust. During the Cultural Revolution, competitions were regarded as elitist and politically incorrect. We all had to be equal but equally good or bad or mediocre? The only good thing you could be was a peasant, a worker or in the armed forces. With a Capitalist Roader mother, I was not welcome in the army.

One moment all my energies had been focused on winning. And then what? With my skating friends, I still had access to the facilities but they were bored by practising for no purpose.

Sara, one of the figure skaters, Shao Fei became an artist and influenced me. She's now married to the writer Bei Dao, who was nominated for the Nobel Prize in literature. Back then, I only knew this slender pretty young woman by sight. Jia heard that she was involved in a project that excited us. We went to meet her at the ice rink.

When she saw us she said,

'Hi, are you two interested in helping us? Guess what – we are rehearsing a show – Red Women's Army on Ice! Want to be in it?' asked Shao Fei.

Sara, I watch you listening to your iPod or playing Japanese computer games. We did have TV and cinema but it wasn't anything you'd enjoy. Documentaries were stilted interviews with heroic workers and interminable political speeches.

Madame Mao's politically correct Model Operas were the most exciting thing on offer but the heroes had no personal feelings, only devotion to the Chairman and the workers and peasants. Madame Mao – what a talent. She had pinched her opera stories from other writers, some of whom she acknowledged, but others she'd silenced. If you remember what happened to Lao She, you will understand why they collaborated with her. That left books not yet culled by the raids of the Red Guards as food for the imagination.

Just imagine the works of Lenin for your bedtime reading? So you can see why Jia and I, girls of your age, were attracted by the prospect of being involved in the production of Red Women's Army on Ice.

The ice dancers in this show were all women so some of the champion boy skaters decided to perform a display of acrobatics on ice during the intervals.

The venue was Beihai (Northern Sea) Stadium, not far from the middle sea area where Chairman Mao lived. The model play was based on a famous story set on Hainan Island. The heroine was a slave in a landlord's home who alone managed to escape when her family was killed. Set on personal revenge, she joins the PLA but comes to see the answer to her grief is to liberate the people. I was in just one scene on the rink and the rest of the time I helped Jia in the box office. We were busy as all the performances were sold-out. Not surprising really, as there was nothing much else to do in the evenings.

But Jia wasn't smiling. She was anxious. Her father had been detained by Red Guards at the university. She had tried to see him but not been allowed. The day before the premiere, he came home limping badly and with black eyes. They had beaten him but let him go.

He told Jia not to worry he would heal and be his old self. But once he was well again, he could be sent to the camp where my mother was working.

I was thrilled that Professor Hu was home and even more thrilled when he lent me his camera and said, 'Little Winter, believe me, you are an artist. Use the camera as if you are creating a scene in a painting.'

My passion for painting and sketching was part of my earliest memories but until then I hadn't thought of myself as an artist. A seed was sown.

Shao Fei skating looked every inch the revolutionary heroine with her fresh face and well-toned body. But I struggled to capture her image on ice –

getting that sense of movement without making her an indistinguishable blur.

As I laid my tired head on my pillow at night, it throbbed with a pang of guilt. While involved with the show my mind had been far away from Weiwei in prison. I pictured his father's black eyes. That thought had my palms sweating as I remembered my interrogation, which could happen again at any time. I persuaded myself that Weiwei would want me to have some relief from fear. After all, for a brief moment, I was an enthusiastic child again.

On the morning of the last performance, Jia came running to me and seemed to be dancing on ice herself.

'He's home. They've let him come home.'

We hugged each other and cried. Then Jia pulled apart and smiled.

'The first thing he plans to do is see the show. He'll be there tonight.'

Sure enough, I caught a glimpse of him in the audience. After the applause died down, I rushed to his exit. How I wanted to hug him but I knew I mustn't. But we did walk back together.

'Yang and the boys were having a high time while ...' he began.

Did he mean to say, 'while I sat on a concrete floor' – but thought the better of it? A few skaters were his friends but he hardly said a word to them about his six months in jail. His face looked pale and much older. But when he saw how happy I was to see him again, he managed a brief smile for me. It was not the smile I knew – his charming boyish smile had disappeared. Weiwei's eyes were unusual; they were large and round like a Westerner but I felt a dagger of anxiety when I saw that they had lost their sparkle.

Mother came home! I was certain that the nightmare was coming to an end at last and life would return to normal. But the reason for her release was not good; she had been injured breaking rocks. I rushed to hug her and she tried to stop me. As I held on to her, she winced with pain and uttered not a word of complaint, but I felt bad for hurting her.

'MaMa! Sorry. How stupid of me. Please what can I do?'

'You can make tea and tell me what you have been doing, that will more than make up for a little discomfort.'

Despite her injuries, she was happy just to be home. I took long deep breaths and hoped this meant the madness was finally over. I wanted life to be like it had been when my parents were respected by everyone, and they could laugh with me.

Red Women's Army on Ice ended leaving me with nothing to do. I stayed in bed longer and longer each morning; partly because I didn't want to let mother out of my sight. Up until her stint of hard labour in the work camp, no hardship had disguised her elegance but that had changed; from then on she always walked with a limp. I pictured her skin as it had once been: smooth as jade and white as porcelain. Now it was roughened and red. I wish I could have hidden my thoughts and feelings of sorrow. She held my hands and looked me in the eyes.

'Xiaodong, you need not look so worried. You can see that I've been ill and when I am better they will send me away again but this time it will be like a rest cure. I'm to go to an agricultural commune. Chairman Mao is concerned that people will go hungry because of all the disruption. Working in the countryside will be good for me and it is good for the country too. You mustn't worry. But you can help me.'

'How Ma? Tell me how.'

'I don't want to worry about you. Your heart and your thoughts hang out for all to see. You must screen them. Keep your thoughts and feelings private. Do you understand?'

I wanted to please and help her but she understood my look of dismay. She said,

'Imagine holding the fan I gave to you. Hold it gracefully in front of your face. Learn to achieve that discretion without its aid. Do it for me.'

She had bought the shining black-spined fan and penned, in her elegant hand, poems for me, down each fold of thick cream paper, one each year until I was fourteen. When I look at it now I can see her gazing straight at me and smiling, her high cheek boned face glowing with love.

In contrast, her demonstration was followed by, 'Promise me?' spoken in a strangely harsh tone, like that of an unkind mother-in-law. 'Promise me?' sounded like an order. I promised and meant it. I tried hard to remember, for mother's sake, but too often remembered too late. I tried to hide my feelings when a month later she had to leave us again. I failed; no fan hid my heartbreak.

Autumn 1967: To the Mountain and Countryside

Sara, gunpowder was invented in China but just used for firecrackers. Chairman Mao's instructions burst like skyrockets on our lives and sent us flying in all directions.

Our leader had total influence and absolute control over all China. An exhortation, a few sentences, or even one single word was called one of Chairman Mao's Supreme Instructions. Unknown to us, Mao was fed up with the chaos and had come up with the solution. He would rid the cities of marauding Red Guards by sending the educated youth to the countryside or mountain areas to be re-educated by the poor and the peasants. He described the countryside of which we were ignorant as a boundless world where the youth of China could reach its maximum potential.

Most of my friends and I were excited about the prospect but despite showing a brave face, I wasn't sure about leaving father and the home and district I had known all my life. I hid my anxiety from my friends and sounding self-assured said, 'I'm bored with all this talk of revolution. I want to do something. I want to get out of Beijing and I don't mind where I go.'

After ten minutes of such talk, we were all united in our desire to go to the countryside, even those who at first had looked anxious. That was how Jia, Weiwei and I together signed up to join the To the Mountain and Countryside Movement.

The first wave was sent to Inner Mongolia where rural areas were organized as People's Communes given ancient Mongolian dynastic names and divided into leagues with banners that seemed so poetic. I visualised myself looking out at a vast expanse of prairie under blue sky and white clouds, creating huge pictures of them somehow merging all the elements. But father was adamant.

'No daughter of mine will go to Mongolia, if I can do anything to prevent it.' He seemed particularly worried because I was a girl. I said, 'Don't worry, Ba. I am strong. All my sports training has given me muscles. Look!' and I showed him. But that didn't seem to be what was concerning him.

'I want to be sure that wherever you go you will be safe.'

He and Weiwei's father shut themselves in his study/bedroom and seemed to talk for ages. Then they came up with a plan. They wanted the three of us to stay together and suggested we go to Manchuria, where there were people who respected Weiwei's father.

'Oh Ba,' I said. 'Can I go south to the sun? Manchuria is soooo cold.'

Seeing our friends off each week, the scene was always the same, with the grief and heroism of possibly one last glance in life. Bored at home, I painted a scene of a spacious platform crowded with people leaving and those seeing them off. I painted what I had seen: some crying, some laughing, some keeping silent and others talking in a frenzied manner. They were so excitable because most were leaving home for the first time – this journey into the unknown was the biggest adventure of their lives so far. As the trains pulled out of the station, many excited looking students began to sing while others looked scared and some seemed sad. They had no idea what to expect of their new life.

I drew passengers, stretching half their bodies out of the windows of the green carriages waving and shouting farewell to the crowds jostling on the platform. In my picture, I had one girl waving the Chinese flag and her earnest idealistic expression could have been mine.

Many of my friends had left Beijing. Would I see them again? With so many of our friends gone, we became impatient, living in a kind of limbo. My heart felt a chill of doubt so I changed my mind about Manchuria and agreed to go. Weiwei and Jia were keen to go north and I would definitely follow Weiwei even if I froze. Weiwei's parents lectured us on how to keep warm in Manchuria and made sure we had good quilts and strong boots.

At last the day arrived for us to venture into Mao's beloved countryside. My father came to see me off but there were few friends because we were among the last to leave. Chairman Mao instructed comrades in rural areas to welcome the educated youths suddenly dumped upon them. What actually went through the minds of the silent peasants, I'm not sure.

Sara, now I understand that To the Mountain and Countryside Movement did alleviate the chaos and reduce the pressure of an aimlessly drifting urban population. Tens of millions of restless young people were all packed off to the countryside where we disappeared. A conjurer had waved a magic wand – that magician was Mao.

The journey north took two days on the hard seats of crowded trains. From our backpacking days we knew how to relax with the rhythm of the train crossing the plains delivering its cargo of the lowest caste: students for re-education.

Eventually we arrived in the town of Hailin about three hundred kilometres east of Harbin. My eye was drawn to the sun hanging low and cool so I wasn't paying attention as I stepped onto the platform. I struggled to keep my balance as I was almost blown away by the biting wind. Our village was forty kilometres away, and from the lorry we looked across a silent landscape with few signs of human life.

When we reached Jiango, over thirty young people had arrived before us. The sexes were separated so Jia and I had to part from Weiwei. We were billeted in the best accommodation because we were the only girls from Beijing. Our wooden hostel was set high against the cliff face, the roof was covered with branches and thick insulating mud. There was a doctor-in-training at our hostel and she was provided with a little office, which was to be her clinic.

The next morning after an early breakfast, we gathered in the courtyard and were told to dance to energise us for the new day. Jia was a good dancer. But I didn't concentrate on my movements; only my eyes darted urgently searching for Weiwei among the self–conscious boys. Every day we saw each other at these assemblies. In front of a portrait of Chairman Mao, we gave our thanks and praised to him for this opportunity to serve our country and further the revolution. Then we broke out into song: The East is Red, the Mao anthem.

The East is Red
The sun rises
China has produced a Mao Zedong
He seeks happiness for the people

So you see Sara, our mornings began with a religious ceremony worshipping not God but Chairman Mao! The singing and dancing was intended to put us in a good mood, a bit like the Seven Dwarfs in the Disney film.

Then winter set in and we headed for the forest behind us. The stars and the moon were etched on the winter sky, glittering in the frozen light. The snow-covered land glowed purple as we walked towards the dark mountain. The snow crunched beneath our feet until the road petered out. From there on we waded through knee-deep drifts from the foot of the mountain and into the woods. I stepped into the deep footprint left by the girl in front of me. We had to edge our way, hand in hand, and the boys were always eager to help the girls and laughed as they spoiled the pristine snow. It was daybreak when at last we arrived at the logging area where we were assigned to work.

As the temperatures plummeted, my eyebrows turned white with drops of ice. Snow-covered Manchuria looked so pure and beautiful and, far from the chaos of the streets of Beijing, I felt safe from political foes. Our enemy in

Manchuria was the weather. When I think about my life as a peasant the indelible memory is of the cold. The winter temperatures fell as low as minus thirty.

Sara it is easy in the USA to buy clothing to protect us against freezing conditions although we don't need them in California, unless we go for fun into the mountains. But in Manchuria our cotton padded jackets and trousers were our only protection from frostbite.

Each winter day we were sent out to chop wood. At night, I liked to draw us looking fragile in the rock hard winter fields. Because of Sports School training, I was fit but Weiwei found it tough at first. The months in prison had weakened him. On rare occasions we were able to talk. Once we were on the same work party and he confided how he had tried Tai Chi in the cell but it was so narrow he couldn't stretch properly.

'Outdoor work feels good after being confined in a little cell.' I felt dreadful. For a moment I had forgotten his time in prison. He ignored the look of shame on my face and said, 'There's something liberating about wilderness,' and waved his arm like a Red Guard. He slowly recovered both his strength and his humour. He said I had got carried away; 'This was not a *little* winter!'

Each evening, back at the cabin, was always the same. Jia and I soaked the blocks of ice we called our feet in hot water to warm them. We made the strangest sounds as we gingerly lowered them in; it was a painful experience. Our next task was to repair our clothes. The branches snagged the material and made holes. To survive the freezing temperatures, we had to patch them carefully each evening. Within weeks, the patches spread across the material like a coloured fungus.

We were able to write home but my mother was still in a work camp in Hebei. I wrote a few careful words to Ba but mostly drew acceptable sketches of my friends as peasants working so the skeletal trees in the background would pass the censors.

But Jia's mother sent a parcel with extra trousers for both of us. Jia grinned and wrapped hers around her neck like a scarf and danced down the dormitory. From then on, when we were really exhausted, we could leave repairs for another day or, even better, wear one pair on top of the other.

Between the girls and boys dormitories was a joint kitchen. Four wood-burning stoves never went out; two were next to the wall of the boys' room and the other two against ours. On top of each stove was an enormous wok. Our regular diet consisted of maize porridge, corn bread and sorghum.

Vegetables were few in this climate so close to Siberia. We kept turnips and cabbage in an outside storeroom but it was like keeping them in a freezer. The few times our diet varied are vivid memories; like the moment we came across a wounded deer and ate meat for the first time in a month.

Our meals may have been frugal, stodgy affairs but after the day's hard labour they tasted good. The time of day I came to love was after we had eaten our evening meal. Some nights Jia and I undid our braids and brushed each other's hair. She became even more like a sister to me. She was the only person I dared confide in. I liked our fellow workers but remembering mother's warning, I had learned to be careful about whom to trust. All sixteen of us found comfort for our aching bodies lying on our kangs.

Sara, kangs are brick beds and are far more comfortable than they sound. They are heated from underneath. The wood-burning stoves in the kitchen had horizontal fire gullies coming out from the back and through the dormitory walls. Each one channelled heat under a row of kangs before the smoke escaped up a chimney at the end of the building.

I laid my bedding roll on the brick and snuggled under my quilt and read poetry while looking out at the unpolluted sky bright with diamonds. The magic couldn't last.

There was nearly always a meeting before sleep. Our work commander announced the details of the work for the next day. This was followed by political study. Our leader was a determined party member. She was about twenty years old and called Chang. She read the latest bulletins to us and was expected to oversee self-criticism. We liked her because she ignored those of us who fell asleep in the shadows. Only if we began to snore did she poke us awake with a stick. Chang liked to talk to Jia and I.

'Jia and Xiaodong went to Hunan and actually touched Chairman Mao's desk. Can you believe it?'

At first, our room-mates didn't believe us. But when we described every detail of the house, they slowly became convinced. Jia was a better actress than me. She was able to put on local accents and gesture like the caretaker who didn't approve when I sat on Mao's chair. Everyone loved Jia; she was good at making people laugh even when life was tough.

Since it was acceptable to tell stories of Mao during politics hour, we repeated our travellers' tale many times over the next two years, embellishing it a little more at each retelling. The caretaker became clownish and we started to gesture more, slapping each other on the back and pretending to fall over and nearly break the chair. Then we would look horrified and get on our knees. Our act became popular with everyone.

As peasants, we worked hard but we were free, unlike the prisoners sentenced for being landlords, Capitalist Roaders and bandits, who toiled alongside us. Wearing labelled black clothes, they had no money and no means of escape in the harsh terrain. When I met them, I smiled at them because I couldn't help thinking of my mother: she was a prisoner like them. My father had said that she was strong. Now I realised what that meant – prisoners were given the hardest and heaviest tasks. They were expected to keep quiet when injured and were not treated with sympathy: they were meant to suffer.

One day Chang called me from the fields.

'Go to Fopin's clinic, she needs some help.'

There had been a fight in the village and two men needed stitching up. They were being kept apart. Fopin was stitching up a leg wound. And she asked if I would clean the hand of the other who was locked in Chang's office.

My patient couldn't have been more than eighteen – he was in serious trouble and looked sullen. I made up my mind not to ask what had happened so that way I could treat him kindly. As I cleaned the gash in his hand, I realised I had never looked at a hand so intensely before and after that always made a point of studying the way they look and move. Our gestures and touch communicate our feelings particularly, anger and compassion, pain and love. That night, I wanted to hold out my hand and touch my mother. A bit of seasonal good fortune would soon make that desire a reality.

We were allowed to return to Beijing to celebrate the Chinese New Year of 1969. On the train home we noticed that we were getting some strange looks. Eyes hovered over our rough-patched clothes. We laughed together as our fellow passengers averted their gaze. We joked that if Lei Feng were in the carriage they would turn their noses up at him. We had been told that the great hero was always ready to share his rations and wore his socks until they were threadbare in order to save the nation's property.

As I walked through the door, my father was there to greet me and grinned from ear to ear, as he looked me up and down.

'Is this really my daughter?'

Red-faced and scruffy, I looked like the peasant I had become. Ba laughed.

'Here is my Little Winter all dressed up for Fridays at the Summer Palace.'

Father looked better; his life had improved a little but he was still under enormous pressure. Then through the door, the next day, came our New Year present. Mother was allowed home for the festivities. Anyone seeing us looking at each other could have thought that we were strangers unless they could see into our hearts. We were looking for hidden injuries but although Ma still limped, she looked better as if she was eating well.

Eager to hear about my life in Manchuria, my parents weren't disappointed. Enthusiasm for my new friends and my occasional paramedic role helping our trainee doctor and stories of the weather in Manchuria, exaggerated only a little, poured out. While we set about making New Year dumplings, we compared notes on life in the countryside. Mother said I was lucky: our Commander Chang was unusually lenient. In most communes, the meetings were long and tedious and anyone not paying attention was punished.

My mother spoke to me as if I were an adult even though I had only just had my seventeenth birthday; for the first time I began to see her as a person and not just my MaMa. She was careful not to say anything political, agreeing with my father like a traditional wife. Physically it was tough but when the time came to return to Manchuria, I was not unhappy. Because we shared the hardship, there was real camaraderie between all of us new peasants.

February 1969: I become a Barefoot Doctor

Sara, I understand why you huddle in your room with your friends after firmly closing the door. After the New Year holiday, Jia and I talked as if we had been separated for years!

Gossip reigned and top of the agenda was news of our 'doctor'. She was being moved on to the county hospital. Fopin had been a student at Beijing Medical School when the People's Dictatorship Committee had taken over the University and her training came to an abrupt end. But in this remote corner of Manchuria, she was among the most qualified in the region. Someone had used common sense. Fopin had worked like us, as a peasant, and was called from the fields only when needed. She was now to work full-time in the county hospital.

Sara, you will find this hard to believe. How can a whole nation become so brainwashed that the hospitals in Beijing were handed over to the military to run while the most senior doctors and administrators were sent for re-education in the countryside or to work as porters?

Fopin tried to keep in touch with teachers at the Medical School but many had been sent to the countryside. One young doctor she knew was still working on the wards and Fopin suppressed a laugh as she trustingly described the situation to me.

'The management of the hospital is in the hands of the Military Propaganda Team. The new head's first decision was to rename the departments. He announced that 'Neurology' or 'Paediatrics' were bourgeois terms so insisted on changing them to correct revolutionary names. The direction signs have been changed to 'Internal Regiments' and 'External Regiments.'

'What is an internal regiment?' I asked.

'He combined Ear, Nose and Throat with Eyes. They are external. Heart, lungs, livers and kidneys are internal. He was so annoyed when patients could not find their way around. The doctors muttered that eyes must be examined in sterile conditions so they can't merge.'

Manchuria was a long way from that epicentre of madness and there, pragmatism was more prevalent. The next bit of news took my breath away. I was to be Fopin's replacement! Chang recommended me because I had often helped her and had a better education than most.

Remember Sara, when the schools closed to real teaching I was not quite fifteen, and now at seventeen I was given so much responsibility!

I felt panicky but Fopin reassured me.

'You went to a good school. You can read and understand well. You will be fine, I promise. You can phone me at the hospital if you need advice.'

Before she set off for Halin, she went through all the medicines in the little clinic. I made a list of the stocks which included dozens of common Western drugs for internal maladies, basic apparatus and drugs for surgery, Chinese medicine tools, such as acupuncture needles, moxa sticks, bulbs and scratching boards. She caught the look of concern on my face at the sight of the needles.

'Look at this chart; it has all the acupuncture points. But start with these ...' and she talked me through the most commonly used ones. Then she handed me a book. During the next two years, like a million others in my position, I came to regard it as my bible. It was *The Barefoot Doctor Manual.*

Although I still had to work in the forest and field, unless called upon, I was given two days off to study the manual. That thick book summarized knowledge of diagnosis and treatment and I read it over and over. As she left, Fopin repeated that I could ring her at the hospital if I was worried about anything.

I'll never forget the day Chang waved to me to leave my work in the fields for my first call out. My head danced with excitement as I made my way to the village. Every family seemed to have a yard enclosed by a plank fence and boarded door, and my patient's house was no exception. As the door creaked on its hinges, I laughed thinking it was the sound of my stomach churning with nerves. In the courtyard, big wooden buttresses and a long-handled axe were placed beside neat piles of firewood. The heavy un-melted snow remained on the roof, filling the cracks and insulating the house. I was greeted by a young woman. She looked carefully at me.

'The patient is my uncle. Are you prepared to treat him?'

I looked surprised at the question.

'Uncle Li has been labelled ...'

I understood. I remembered a man hanging from a tree.

'Show me to him.'

He was in bed but on the chair beside the bed was his tunic and on it the sign for landlord. But he was a poor man. In the drive to attack counter-revolutionary elements he had been accused of being a landlord – a crime in sixties China. The old man looked sorry for himself as he complained of cramps and diarrhoea. But I was pleased because I felt confident I could deal with his ailment. I prescribed bright coloured Bitter Yellow Lotus pills to stop the flow. His niece came to find me a few days later smiling and thanked me; I was so proud.

The following week a young woman of about twenty-four came to see me. She was pregnant. No sooner had she left the clinic than I read and re-read the sections on pregnancy and birth but I still did not feel confident about this condition. I was so embarrassed. I knew I had been lucky at fourteen, when my periods began, that mother was at home. She had prepared me and said when it happened I had left childhood behind and become a woman. Although it still came as a shock, I made the transition to adulthood but, after my mother was sent to labour camp, I had no one to ask about more complicated things. I was an urban girl. I had not even seen animals born. Reading the manual, I realised how ignorant I was. I didn't really know how babies were made but I was a little more aware of the hazards of giving birth and knew about mothers dying. I decided to ring Fopin for advice.

That night, I whispered to Jia on the next kang. She knew more than me. One thing was made very clear, a good female comrade was expected to devote all her time and energy to the people and the revolution. She was not to think of marriage until her late twenties.

I can see a snapshot in my mind. The frame is vague but the vivid image is of Weiwei, his arm pouring with blood. He had accidently cut it wielding his axe and was bought to the clinic. I was nervous as I washed it carefully. He needed a couple of stitches. I was able to treat it and bandaged his arm. It seemed to take me a long time as I wove the bandage lovingly till it looked neat and beautiful. His friend standing beside him admired the herring bone pattern.

'Comrade Weiwei, you should have a week off manual labour. I can give you a chit for the supervisor. Come every day so I can check the wound is healing and change your bandages,' I said in a quiet slow voice.

My barefoot doctor status meant I was listened to respectfully. But there was a glint of an additional pleasure in Weiwei's expression. I knew he would come every day and no one would think anything of it. His next appointment was the first time we had been completely alone together. Once we had shaken hands but now I was shaking.

The next day began like every other one, long before sunrise. Breakfast was provided as dawn broke and we often worked until sunset. That day, returning from the fields, a golden sunset rained over a multi-coloured carpet. I had to stop and take in the scene spread out before me. The beauty of my surroundings transfixed me. Streams gurgled down the pristine mountains as I walked across a field of wild flowers just about to open. I bent down and picked one. I gently peeled back the red petals. It felt like my heart was unfurling like the flower. After washing and eating, I went to the clinic and waited for Weiwei.

'Can I come in, Doctor?' He handed me a bunch of white wild flowers with a single red bloom in the middle. I gazed at them for a long time taking in every petal and then pulled myself together.

'Oh, Weiwei. Have we been sucked up in a whirlwind? You are older than me. This is crazy. All these dignified peasants consulting me and I'm just seventeen and a half. What would our grandparents have thought? We would have been beaten for presuming to teach our elders. But come here. Let me look at you ...'

Weiwei, the confident hero, looked shy but he held out his arm. I stroked the bandage and teased off the end, then slowly unwound it and with each turn I brushed his skin. He looked at me. I had never looked so deeply into anyone's eyes before. He liked it.

His wound looked clean but I cleaned it again and treated it with antiseptic, leaning over him as I worked. My tiny tight breasts rubbed against him and he began to breathe faster. As I re-wound the bandage, I found myself trembling.

There was a knock on the door. In came work commander Chang.

'You are needed in the village comrade Xiaodong.' She looked at us suspiciously. I was not afraid because she was not unkind but I knew what had happened was dangerous.

Oh Sara, how can you possibly understand that fear? You and your friends live so freely, perhaps too freely. Rather than I explain it, please read on and eventually you will understand. You get stroppy but underneath, I know you are not insensitive. I shout at you too much.

My heart was still beating fast when I listened to the village woman's heart and lungs and didn't hear anything wrong. Everything seemed fine but the patient sounded ill. Now that I understood about pregnancy, I quietly asked her if she had missed a period. She nodded. I told her she must rest and eat well and she beamed at me. Darkness fell as I returned to the dormitory.

Sara, you don't how black night can be. Here in Berkeley there are street lights, car lights and the lights of San Francisco below.

In 1969 in Manchuria there were only the stars and moon to illuminate the way. When they were obscured by cloud, walking at night was treacherous. On the way back from the village, I tripped several times and fell on wet ground. Exhaustion evaporated some of my fear. I collapsed on my kang and was grateful for the extra trousers Jia's mother had sent. I fell asleep the second my head hit the pillow. I was not excused from the pre-dawn start the following day because spring is such a busy time in the countryside. Because of my name, I have an imaginative attachment to the seasons but in those years my whole life and being seemed to flow with the seasonal changes.

In spring, men and women, old and young, wore a bag filled with seeds around their necks and walked across the fields at arm's length from each other. As we swung our arms to scatter the soya bean seed, even in our shabby clothes, we looked beautiful; like some troupe dancing the rite of spring followed by the plough which, in a rhythmic movement, nudged the earth over the seeds to bury them. That's it, I thought, nature has a rhythm and we peasants are part of that ever-turning wheel. When we stopped for lunch,

Chang pulled me aside and whispered,

'I'm sending Weiwei home on leave due to his injury.'

Weiwei's injury was not serious. Within a week, he could have been back in the fields. A surge of purple anger and disbelief spread through my body. I couldn't hide it. My heart seemed to lose a beat but I tried to control my feelings as I had before the People's Dictatorship Committee. Chang was not like them. I had always found her strong but kind and an energetic singer who tried to inspire us to work hard. But when I stood with the crowd who waved him off, I almost hated her.

Sara, it was such an innocent situation but I know now that Chang aimed to protect herself and me. I didn't realise that at the time – I was ignorant of the danger we could have brought upon ourselves and on Chang.

The snows melted and the temperatures rose and I was faced with a new enemy – insects. We suffered terribly from midges in the early morning, and large wasps during the day. There was never a quiet time. In the evening, when the midges ceased their tormenting, the mosquitoes had no mercy so I was kept busy treating infected bites.

Up until now there was one procedure I had avoided. I was nervous about acupuncture – after all, it involved sticking needles in patients. Chang complimented me on the good job I did cleaning and bandaging wounds and prescribing medicines but asked why I didn't use acupuncture. I made excuses but when alone with Jia, I confided my lack of confidence. 'What if I hurt someone?' Jia laughed and said I could practise on her. Placing the needles carefully using an anatomical chart, I tried not to look into my friend's eyes. After I finished with her and I took a step back, Jia looked like the arrowed chart. I took the needles out even more carefully than I had put them in. Jia grinned her magic grin,

'I am not sure if you'll make a good doctor, Jie Jie, you seem a bit nervous but you are great masseur. I feel so relaxed that you'd better help me to my kang.'

Happy in the knowledge that I hadn't hurt her, I tried out my newly acquired skills on the villagers. My first patient was a woman of about thirty-five who said her headache was so bad she could hear it. After the acupuncture, she turned to me with a beaming smile. How I loved my work! The students and the villagers seemed to confide in me and left nothing hidden. I thought about Beijing where people were tight-lipped and where I tried to keep my mouth shut without succeeding all of the time. I revelled in the frankness. It was as refreshing as the pure air we breathed.

Weiwei wrote to Jia every week and carefully sent messages for me. The Party read all letters: everyone was expected to spy on everyone else. Except, where we were, it was different – our common enemy, the climate bonded us. One of his letters was very strange, almost poetic.

Look to the stars.
Look to the moon.
Never the same again.

Jia giggled.

'I'm sure of one thing. My brother will never make a poet.'

'What was that code for?'

A few days later Chang came to the clinic and spoke in a voice with harsh tones,

'Weiwei will be joining us again for the harvest.'

Nothing more was spoken, but her warning look towards me said it all. Revolutionary youth could have no one in their heart – no one except Chairman Mao. When her face grew tense, as she gave me a second piercing look, I knew that those eyes had seen something awful. Years later I guessed the truth. We heard stories of executions of rapists but the reality about many of them was hidden. Those 'rapists' were often just young lovers who happened to be caught. Pressure was applied to the girls to denounce the boys, and they innocently succumbed not realising the cruel consequences. Now, I forever remember Chang with affection but not then. I resented her for wanting to separate Weiwei and me.

That was not the only hidden truth. When Weiwei returned in August he had an incredible story to tell; the story behind his poor poetry. We longed to talk freely so when Chang wasn't looking, we carried our bowls of noodles outside in the warm evening sun and sat on a log outside the hostel. My eyes shifted from the orange setting sun to the mysterious silver new moon until my gaze settled on Weiwei's round eyes.

Jia and I listened spellbound to his news but I tried hard not to look him in the eye. Together again, all three of us brimmed with pleasure that was hard to disguise. For me, he brought news of my father. He had been working at the National Academy of Science and Weiwei said he was stressed to breaking point when a contingent of young soldiers was billeted at the vast campus with orders to re-educate the scientists. 'Guess what they had been asked to do?' whispered Weiwei.

'Self-criticism? Confessions?' I suggested.

'That too, but they were also ordered to discredit Einstein! On my first visit to your father he came home looking tense and anxious.' He paused and sighed.

'You're sure right, Chowy, he told me about the interminable confessions and the lectures on *The Thoughts of Chairman Mao*. But July 20th was different. Your Ba came to our home with a broad grin on his face and sent me out to buy wine. I can't remember when my father last did that. He poured out two glasses and took his to the window, looked up and said, "Let us make a toast: To the first man on the moon!" It was so good to see him joking and teasing me with silly stories after the years of tension and fear – it felt like man to man – it was such a good feeling. He placed his elbow on the table and leaned over, trying but failing to talk quietly. This is what he told me:

"All of us, the entire academy and the PLA propaganda team went to the theatre today to watch a film. I was bored. You can guess what I expected. The head of the propaganda team stood up and my brain, which had been somewhere else, suddenly woke up when he said, 'This film will show you what the Americans are doing. We must criticise this. Don't be taken in by them: it's not special. This project is just another dirty way of making money to further the capitalist ideal.'" Your father looked animated but he wasn't drunk when he said,

"Riveted to my seat, my eyes hardly blinked as the film started to roll and showed a spaceship called Apollo orbiting the moon. I couldn't believe what was before my eyes. A module drifted down onto the surface, steps were lowered and down them walked a man in a space suit. His booted foot was on the moon! His words were 'One small step for man'. I still can't believe it. But it's true, Weiwei. It is true. Come to the window. Look up there. A man has walked there. A man has walked on the moon so anything is possible." He waved his glass at the silver satellite, spilling some wine on his Mao tunic. I swear he giggled like a schoolgirl – sorry girls, I didn't mean that. Forgive me, Chowy but I thought your father must be crazy because unusually for him he kept on talking. I had the impression that since your Ma was taken away he had barely opened his mouth except to eat, so this was great. He said,

"It was hard for me and my comrades to contain our excitement but with all those soldiers around us, we had to keep silent. How we managed to do so I'll never know. They haven't reported it in *The People's Daily.* They haven't shared this news with the country. The only people in China who know are some scientists and a few platoons of soldiers – and some of them fell asleep! And now YOU know! I expect the others will be talking to their families; they won't be able to keep it to themselves. So be careful Weiwei. If you say anything, they could accuse you of spreading capitalist propaganda and believing that Einstein is right!"

'I'll be honest with you, girls. At first, I didn't believe your father, Chowy. But the soldiers left the campus and he was fine and he still believed it, so there may be something in it.'

Jia replied, 'Our father said the United States is advanced scientifically and technologically and according to him, Premier Zhou Enlai wants China to modernise but The Gang threaten him all the time. Do you remember the story he told us about one of his comrades? He said,

"Yeh Du Pei was lured back from the States to help develop science but one look at the poor man and you see he bitterly regrets his decision to return. I shouldn't talk like this to you, this is dangerous talk. But I am lucky I have son who thinks for himself. Too many parents are afraid of their children." '

Weiwei became silent but Jia and I sat as if we were glued to the log outside the hostel. After a while, I asked him about life in Beijing. That is when I learned how lucky we were. Weiwei told terrible stories of the fear that came from rivalry and jostling for power. The way to advance was by identifying enemies. This had been happening everywhere.

'Surely, since the war ended, things have got better?' I asked.

Sara, the war I was referring to was little more than a skirmish. But as a result of it, Mao won support and my mother won her release.

This was the famous Zhenbao Island battle. Zhenbao Island lies on the border river between the Soviet Union and China. The two armies opened fire to fight for the territorial right of the island. They engaged with machine-guns, artillery and tanks. Some people think the Chairman provoked the attack deliberately to whip up a nationalist fervour. But even Mao saw that the chaos destroying industry and society could not continue and he asked, 'Is this endless quarrelling necessary?'

We were ordered to prepare for war with our old friends, now our enemy, the Soviet Union. No one could talk of anything else as the tension rose when we were told that the Soviet Union had stationed more than a million troops and thousands of tanks along the Chinese border. Judging from the map, our village was not far from the border. Of course Mao's strategy worked; no matter how complicated the domestic situation was, once there was a state emergency, everyone rallied around to fight against the common enemy.

Once again, Mao had secured the support of the people, and China was under his firm control. The war was brief and, with his position assured, Mao decided to rehabilitate lots of Capitalist Roaders so the country could function a little better. Even in Manchuria we felt the thaw and I desperately hoped my parents would be among the chosen.

The one telephone in the entire village hung on the wall and needed winding. The postmaster received a phone call message from my father saying that I must return to Beijing. New Year 1970 was not far away so this summons worried me. Could my parents be ill or was there a sudden bad turn of events?

The sun shone brightly the next day when I received a letter from my mother. I could hardly believe it; she hadn't been allowed to write to me before. I read it over and over again. She was going to be allowed home. She had been re-educated and was no longer a Capitalist Roader. The University was going to re-start some traditional courses. My mother was to teach English as well as Russian. She wrote,

'I wish I was more proficient in English but I am happy, Xiaodong. It is a good way to serve the country. I shall be allowed home for the New Year celebrations and then will not return to the camp. I am counting the days until I see you and your BaBa again.'

Waving the letter, I ran to Jia shouting, 'I'll see her soon. We'll be together even before the New Year.'

I handed my Barefoot Doctor Manual to Jia and left her in charge of the clinic.

'See you soon.' I waved to Jia and my fellow peasants as I left on a lorry bound for Harbin and the train to Beijing. Through the window, I viewed a world in which I did not seem to belong. I was like a spirit suspended in limbo observing my surroundings as if from another world. But once I caught the number 3 trolley bus that all changed. The more I looked around me, the more a sense of belonging swept over me. 'I am on my way home. This is home.'

I ran up the dusty stairs and opened the doors shouting,

'I am home Ba, I'm home.'

My father was sitting on the sofa; his head in his hands and ... He was crying. I had never seen him cry before.

'Ba, what is it? What is wrong?'

He took me in his arms and held me so tightly that I thought I would suffocate. Then he let me go. He didn't look at me.

'Your mother is dead. Bo Lin is dead.'

'That can't be right. She said she's coming home.'

'The truck taking her to the town to catch the train turned over. The road was pot-holed. The driver ... I could kill him.'

Father clenched his fists so hard that his nails drew blood.

'He was drunk – the idiot was drunk – driving on those narrow mountain bends. The truck plunged off the road into the ravine. Everyone was killed. The people in the bus following saw it all happen, he was driving too fast.

Sorrow

I don't know how we got through the funeral. Ba thought we should take her ashes to the town of her birth but I said,

'Wouldn't mother want to be buried here so we can visit her on Tomb-sweeping Day?' He agreed. So we took her little urn to the cemetery near The Summer Palace where she had been happy. It looked so tiny for such a big personality. I needed something to help me feel her presence. Ma loved poetry; she told me it helped in the labour camp. It focused her mind elsewhere and to another time where she could forget that she was wielding a pickaxe and shovel.

I needed words and words of love. I bought a paper fan and with brush and ink wrote her name in as beautiful letters as I could create.

By her little grave, I set the fan alight with the joss sticks and watched the smoke rise with her spirit. I prayed those words would accompany her into the afterlife. I knew Ba didn't believe in the afterlife or the ancient rituals. He thought grave goods even if burnt were superstitious but said not one word of criticism. I had lost my mother and if it helped me, he would not object. So I prayed and promised to look after her in the afterlife.

The flat seemed so empty. I shut myself in my room. I took out the cream fan she had given me on my thirteenth birthday. She had chosen poems for me, one for each of the years of my life and penned them in her own hand along each spine. I examined every brushstroke. Each one was a moment of time in my life until that birthday. Yes that birthday, when she gave it to me, was just before our lives descended into hell.

As I re-read each poem, I began to cry. At the cemetery my eyes had stayed dry. In my hands were her precious words, her spirit; I sobbed and then screamed. Father ran into the room.

'Oh Ba, look what I've done. My tears have smudged Mama's beautiful calligraphy. I've ruined it.'

Father stroked my faced wiping away the tears and said, 'Little Winter, you have not ruined it. Those are tears of love. Your mother is remembered in them as well as in her writing. Keep it safe always. Whenever you take it out and read it, you will remember the good time when she wrote it for you and the teardrops will remind you of this bad time.'

I folded it carefully and wrapped it in a silk scarf, one she had owned before the Cultural Revolution and had managed to preserve. I held it near my face and hoped it held her scent but I smelled nothing.

'Ba, help me always to remember her.'

'I won't need to, Little Winter. Every time you pick up a paintbrush you will remember her. Art to Bo Lin was another dimension and she held your baby hand to help you make your first strokes.'

Part 2: THE DRAGON YEARS

The IPG

That year, 1970, we didn't celebrate the New Year. I tried closing my ears and eyes to the sound of the fireworks. Ba dragged himself back to work but I didn't want to leave him. He seemed to shrink after my mother died. I wrote to Chang, and the Party gave me permission to stay in Beijing to look after my father. But what was I to do with myself? I couldn't be a barefoot doctor in Beijing.

I secretly rediscovered art; I sketched ordinary things – not Chairman Mao not Lei Feng, but a stool, a chair, a table with a pot of flowers, the cabbages on the stairs and Ba reading a book. I dreamed up tempting dishes using seasonal vegetables and the monthly rations allowed each person – two pounds of pork, two pounds of oil (and seven boxes of matches!)

One day after eating our meal in silence, Ba suddenly banged a fist on the table and spoke with fierce determination.

I hope you haven't forgotten all the leaders' names, Sara, or you won't understand what my father was talking about.

'Things must change. Zhou Enlai has a plan to introduce Four Modernisations. We must develop science and technology, and apply them to industry, defence, agriculture and education. At this moment, it's difficult for him but the country must change, it will change. It has to change – our economy has been ruined.'

He consciously lowered his voice and leaned forward close to me and said,

'Chairman Mao keeps three puppets. Dangling at the end of his strings are Lin Biao with control of the army and Prime Minister Zhou Enlai whom he needs because of his administrative abilities and the other is his wife, Jiang Qing. He wants them to fight and struggle with each other: that way he maintains his power. But The Chairman is starting to realise that we need to modernise so Zhou's position must improve and the nation will celebrate.'

'Why are you telling me this, Ba?' I asked.

'You must be ready to study hard. Soon the Universities will teach again and not just be centres of political in-fighting. If you get permission to be a student, you must learn English. English is the language of science. We shall need it. For now, you will have to teach yourself but you are a clever girl, Little Winter, you can do it.'

'Ba, won't it be hard to learn English without a teacher? Won't they expect me to work?'

'Let me think and see what can be arranged.'

A few days later, father said I should go down the road and call on the China International Publishing Group to see if they would employ me as a graphic designer. I was so nervous. Why should such a prestigious organisation be interested in me?

I discovered that the situation at IPG was as strange as everywhere else in China. Chun Chan Yeh, the editor of Chinese Literature, a monthly journal in English and French, had recently been employed mostly emptying latrines. How could that happen to the only Chinese member of the Bloomsbury Group; a writer whose Mountain Village was named one of the best writings of 1947 by the English Book Society? I remembered what had happened to Lao She, our greatest playwright. At least Chun Chan Yeh was alive.

My security dossier was not too bad despite my run in with The People's Dictatorship Committee. Chang had sent a glowing report of my time as a barefoot doctor. I had forgiven her for parting Weiwei and me. The IPG liked my artistic skills and took me on!

Chun Chan Yeh was given time off his cleaning duties to translate the thoughts of Chairman Mao and other propaganda material for use abroad. I wanted to talk to him about how to learn English but like most people his age, he was rather wary of me. Who could blame anyone of his generation for feeling like that? Yet, he knew we were not really to blame.

I was assigned work illustrating books and pamphlets in the style art historians call Socialist Realism: young pigtailed peasants waving the red flag and following Chairman Mao across a field of ripe corn.

You get the picture, Sara? It may not be great art but I felt so lucky. Until this time, I had never thought of art as a career. Before the Cultural Revolution, if you had asked me, 'what do you want to be?' I might have answered, 'an ice skater.' Being selected for Sports School was a big deal but the political upheaval had brought it to an abrupt end. Art had always been a part of me: like eating or breathing. I wouldn't be me without a brush or an eye. What would I have chosen to do, if I could have seen where 'art' as a career would take me? I don't know the answer to my own question. But I do know that the urge to draw what I see is there every day and has been since I could pick up a pencil.

After work, I would amble home and buy vegetables on the way. I serrated the edges of carrots and cut them in flower shapes and arranged the sliced vegetables like a picture to entice Ba's appetite. One night, while complimenting me on the meal, he said,

'Little Winter, I have something for you', and handed me a Chinese/English dictionary. He was serious about me teaching myself English. But how could I learn from a dictionary? I couldn't understand the script and had no idea of the pronunciation. Then, at work, I found a pamphlet comparing the sounds of English letters to Chinese and was allowed to take it home. Although my father was unusually demonstrative for a Chinese man, I knew he was serious. With the help of the pamphlet I studied hard in my spare time because I so wanted to please him. I struggled and made very slow progress and I missed my friends.

September 1971: An epic plane crash.

Everyone looked stunned but no one dare talk about it. You wouldn't think the People's Daily an exciting read but that day was different.

Do you remember, Sara, the rally in Tiananmen Square in 1966, when Lin Biao spoke for The Chairman himself and launched The Cultural Revolution to over a million eager teenagers, including me?

Now Lin Biao, the great leader, was dead and not being mourned but condemned as the vilest specimen of traitor and hypocrite. How could this be? I rushed home to ask the only person I could talk to about it, my father. Lin Biao had been his commander during the Civil War but even he wouldn't talk about it.

Can you understand how confusing was that?

There was an occasional whisper followed by an abrupt silence at work. I suspected that some of my colleagues knew something; they looked uneasy and speechless. It was only after Mao died that I learned the truth from friends involved in an underground magazine.

Sara, we can't choose our parents – you probably wouldn't have chosen me if you had any choice in the matter. But when you discover what Lin Biao's daughter did, you will see how lucky I was that my parents taught me to think and that, of my closest friends, Weiwei had a mind of his own.

The army was the one organisation that held Mao's empire together. Lin Biao sensed that Mao no longer trusted him because of his popularity in the army. He must have guessed his fate; after all he had colluded in the downfall of Liu Shao-chi and Deng Xiao Ping. He did not intend to wait around to suffer.

Lin Biao and his son, Tiger, planned a coup starting with an attack on the Imperial Fishing Villa where Madame Mao was living. Mao was making a tour of inspection in the south and the idea was to blow up the train taking him to Shanghai. But their plot failed and they attempted a hurried escape to Hong Kong via Guanzhou (Canton). Tiger made a fatal mistake. He told his sister Dodo to be ready to leave the next morning. Dodo was completely brainwashed and did as we had been taught. She put love of Mao above love of her family.

You'll find this difficult to understand Sara. How could a daughter do this to her parents and her brother? But it was not unheard of.

She reported them to the Praetorian guards stationed in a separate building at the end of their drive. Lin, his wife and son Tiger were pursued as they boarded their plane, which hurriedly took off, without refuelling and with a new destination, not Canton but Outer Mongolia. They died in the plane crash that followed.

Strangely, it meant that my father's wish started to come into being because Mao had to replace Lin Biao and needed someone the people could trust, so he brought back Deng Xiao Ping, and even Zhou Enlai's influence increased.

Jia and Weiwei were allowed back to Beijing. Although food was rationed, I saved up so that I could invite them around for a celebratory meal! We talked and talked well into the night. I wanted news about everyone in the village.

Jia had plenty to say because she had taken over my post. Like me, she had grown to love working as a barefoot doctor.

'What will you do now, Jia?' I asked.

'I want to become a proper doctor. I'm going to The Medical School in the morning – no, later today. It's wonderful being together again ... the three of us. I could talk till dawn.'

In silence, Weiwei bit his lips. He couldn't share his sister's joy. Because of his history and unfavourable dossier, he had to report every month to the Beijing Security Bureau. We arranged to meet in Beihai Park. It had been a place of refuge when the chaos had begun and it was almost nostalgic walking by the north bank of the lake and then veering off into the garden within a garden, the Quieting Heart Room once again. Weiwei looked at me longingly. I smiled but felt weak. What could we do? Why was life so complicated? Jia was like a sister and understood. She waved to a friend and they walked a little ahead of us so we could talk alone. But it wasn't a romantic conversation, Sara, and we couldn't touch each other. What a crazy world we lived in!

'So, how was the interview?' I whispered.

He lit a cigarette and inhaled slowly before saying,

'Not so bad. I've to report every month but they've found me work as a photographer on *The People's Daily.*'

'Wow! That sounds exciting.'

'I only wish it was, Snowdrop.'

Snowdrop was Weiwei's special name for me and I called him Hero. It was our tiny taste of personal life.

Weiwei continued, 'Life in the countryside was tough but we were left pretty much alone in Manchuria. Eyes will be on me twenty-four hours a day at *The People's Daily*. You know who's in control?'

'I know of the man, Yao Wenyuan. He calls himself a literary critic. Yao Wenyuan and Madame Mao are about as creative as flies in a tunnel. How did they do it? How did The Gang get so much power?'

'Your father can probably answer that better than me. I'll have to be constantly wary – the little swine will be suspicious of me. The only reason I've been given this job is that I'm a good photographer and they want to be flattered with fine pictures of themselves. They don't mind me looking but they don't want me thinking, Snowdrop.'

He threw his cigarette stub on the ground and crushed it with his right shoe.

Soon after that, something wonderful happened, an opportunity to look and see something new. A friend at the office gave me a book wrapped in brown paper and told me not to open it until I got home. What could it be? I could hardly wait until home time. Sitting at our table that evening, I turned the pages on western art from the Renaissance until Rembrandt. For the first time I saw sketches by Michelangelo and Leonardo. There was something different about them from Chinese drawing – the light and shade. I stared and stared at the portraits – then rushed into the bedroom and brought out a mirror. I propped it up in front of me, and tried a self-portrait in the Western manner. Over and over again I tried until I felt I had got it right. Even so this girl's eyes were looking directly into mine and it was unsettling. She wasn't like me smiling or laughing but serious. I began to cry; I looked like my mother.

1972: The door is ajar.

I couldn't wait to discuss art with Weiwei. I suggested we meet at Nine Dragon Wall. The nine dragons play with clouds and I felt like that. I had a new inspiration and I wanted to toss it about. I wondered if I could let glimmers of it into my work at the publishing house. I asked Weiwei what he thought.

'Maybe you can colour the sky, Snowdrop, but on the ground make sure the valiant workers wave the right flags.'

He laughed and then his face turned grey and stiff.

'What's the matter?' I asked.

'You know what the matter is. My only freedom is to angle my camera to make them look good.'

Weiwei had a great eye for composition but at *The People's Daily* he was treated like dirt. His job was regarded as unsuitable for an intellectual. I never met anyone so keen to learn as Weiwei. In his spare time, he was rarely without a book but his books were not like mine. He even taught himself physics. Where he found them I don't know, but I saw him with books on Daoism and Buddhism of the kind that were burned by Red Guards.

However clever he was, there was no career ladder for him: once a photographer, always a photographer. Trying to focus on becoming a good technician was his best distraction from the stifling and dangerous place he inhabited. Then one day something happened to make Weiwei excited about his work. He actually looked optimistic when he met me.

'I can't believe it, the President of the United States is coming to Beijing!'

Weiwei rushed to check the rota every day to see which photographer was assigned to which job. Nixon's meetings with The Chairman were sensitive so Weiwei was not chosen to photograph them. Ba explained why only very trusted people would be used.

'Mao is ill with Lou Gehrig's disease. His speech is slurred and will get worse. They won't record him talking, they'll just use pictures.'

Father was right – the historic handshake was shown on the television news but no conversation.

Weiwei was on the rota when Nixon, accompanied by Premier Zhou Enlai, made a visit to the Great Wall. He loved this assignment and I bathed in his rare smiles. It gave him scope for artistic shots and he was so close to the leaders.

'I feel that I've witnessed something momentous,' he said but the smile vanished as suddenly as it had appeared. 'But I'm worried about the Premier. I'm sure he's ill. He looked exhausted.'

Sara, Zhou Enlai had his faults but he was a pragmatist and had charisma. At that time, he was our only hope of change for the better.

I wanted to see Weiwei smile again and again. Weiwei was better than me at keeping his thoughts hidden but when he relaxed with me and was happy, his face looked so different. How could I catch that moment with a paint brush or pen? I had an idea.

'It is ages since I've been to the Great Wall; not since I was ten. Do you think you can take me?'

My reward was an indulgent nod of agreement and a promise to organise a trip. An impressive section of The Great Wall lies very close to Beijing but in those days the only way to get there was by bus or bike. Weiwei suggested a group of us cycle there on our next weekend off, hoping the weather would be kind to us. Planning something we could control felt so good. A bit of rebellion stirred in me. I was safe with my friends and planned some illegal sketches of the views from the wall without a single heroic worker in sight! Because we were cycling, we headed for the nearest section, which is not the most impressive.

Our bikes were not like your streamlined titanium streak of lightning, Sara, but we were happy to take our time.

The fifty kilometres to Juyongguan took us over four hours on our slow bikes. We arrived in time for a late lunch of noodles. There was a shop in the approach selling prints and books. In the window, in pride of place, was a print of an oil painting by Liu Chunhua called *Mao on the way to Anyun, 1921*. My friends were surprised when I asked them to wait while I bought a copy. This print went on to be possibly the best selling print of all time, selling more than a billion copies – more than the population of China in the seventies. This was the moment of its release. It shows a young and fresh-faced Mao, brimming with studious idealism, against a gorgeous background of mountains and dreamy clouds in a bright blue sky. I loved the background – so different from the average propaganda art. But that was not my reason for buying it. I asked the shopkeeper to roll it up.

After the bike ride and climbing up three steep sections, I began to slow. As a skater and a peasant I'd been so fit but my now sedentary life was not so healthy. With each step I resolved to do something about it. Weiwei saw me slowing down and held back, waving the others on.

'We'll keep a look out for barbarians for a while.'

Wang stretched his eyes and made a scary face and we all laughed. Weiwei and I watched as the others carried on up the undulating wall. Each section ended in a watchtower and he pointed inside one. Today, the wall crawls with thousands of tourists every day but in those days, there were no foreign tourists, apart from organised groups from communist countries. And few Chinese had the opportunity to travel except home for New Year. So Weiwei and I were quite alone. My eyes closed and my head rested on his shoulder. Stroking my hair, Weiwei said,

'I have always wanted to see what you look like asleep. I'll sing you to dreamland.'

'That will be lovely …'

But I couldn't sleep; I could feel Weiwei's heart beating. I turned my head to look at him. He looked down at me. His eyes seemed to be consuming me.

'Please don't. I …' and he kissed me. I could hardly breathe.

'I love your skin – silky as gossamer. My delicate little snowdrop.'

Each touch sent me trembling with pleasure but Weiwei began to look agitated.

'Snowdrop, as soon as they will let us, will you marry me?'

'Will they let us, Weiwei?'

He didn't get the chance to answer because the others were descending quickly towards our tower; down being much easier than up. It would be a while before we were able to be alone like this again.

Sara, you will think this is no big deal but you would be wrong. It was huge. Weiwei and I had known each other nearly all our lives and we had never kissed before. If you are ever able to visit China you will notice that people don't kiss on the street.

That time in Paris when I was uncomfortable with its ritual kiss on the cheeks you'd asked me, 'Mummy, why are you so cold to people?' Some cultural things are hard to change and personal things like that are probably the hardest. Intimacy means more in private. That is what the word 'intimate' means. It's private. You don't have to copy me: you are an American girl.

Our friends sat around and teased me about the print I had bought. I took out my pens and unrolled it. I untidied Mao's neat hair and opened his eyes bright and wide and they saw what I saw – my Weiwei. 'Be careful Chowy, you'd better roll it up quick.' But they smiled knowingly. They knew that Weiwei was my hero, like Mao was everyone else's.

The Cultural Revolution had passed its most brutal stage but it was still dangerous to deface the image of Mao. But how could I resist?

Sara, my heart was beating fast but we couldn't even tell our friends about our intentions. This was before the one-child policy; nonetheless, the government was anxious about the growing population. You needed permission to marry, not just from your parents but from your workplace and also from the Communist Party. With an illegal marriage, you would lose your job. The government didn't want young people to marry until the guy was in his late twenties but girls could try for permission in their mid-twenties. Just imagine how that felt. We were young and in love. Even I was young once!

1976: The Year of the Dragon

People froze in shock, like water suddenly turned to ice in the blast of bitter winter weather blanketing northern China. All my life, Zhou Enlai had held the post of Prime Minister. Amid all the upheavals, his had been the hand that tried to steady the ship of state and now he was dead. Weiwei was upset and could not suppress his anger.

'Everywhere people are crying. You'd think the whole of *The People's Daily* would be given over to a reflection of his life. I met Chanliang – you know – from China TV. His handsome face was contorted by the struggle to obey orders. They had started to make commemorative programmes, a tribute to his life, but our overlord ....' Weiwei found it hard to say his name; a whisper of criticism invited danger. Then he remembered that he was safe with me and almost spat out,

'Yao Wenyuan issued orders for singing and dancing programs to be broadcast! Can you believe it? On the way out of China TV, angry crowds swore at Chanliang and I don't blame them. He said he felt ashamed, ignoring their grief. But what can we do, we minions in the media? If Chanliang or I said anything they would sack us; probably arrest me. I should be photographing the people mourning but that's not permitted, and I heard and saw too much in prison to want to go back there. What would that be like for Jia and my parents? Oh Snowdrop, what can I do?'

Weiwei's face brightened up slightly as he remembered the response of viewers to the broadcast musical.

'People have found a new way to express themselves. They turned off their TVs.'

'They can't punish them for not watching TV ...or can they?' I asked.

'This feels different, Snowdrop, but be careful, please.'

This kind of resistance was new. Mao and his cronies suspected that Zhou was genuinely mourned and respected. He was hard working and intelligent and people understood and forgave him for not being able to stop the excesses of the Cultural Revolution. The Gang of Four didn't even want to mark his death so his funeral was a low-key affair using an ordinary bus to transport the body. Disappointment hung in the air and a bitter anger because people thought it disrespectful, even insulting.

January and February came and went and still there was no state memorial. Some friends organised an unofficial memorial service. A note was made of anyone attending, including me. Neighbourhood spies were asked by the Gang of Four to report anyone who cried and I cry easily. The next day at work, my boss called me in. He'd had a visitor from the Security Bureau.

'Little Winter, be careful: I'd like to but I've no way of protecting you. Whatever you do, don't be seen with tears in your eyes. Smile at your neighbours; I'm sure you know which ones.'

While he was speaking the sky turned black and there was a tremor. We rushed outside thinking it was an earthquake but a comet had struck China. It was the largest ever to hit earth. The 3000 pieces of comet fell out of the sky on March 8th. The largest weighed 1,170 kilos. Chinese people are a bit superstitious about events like that and I was too. Since it came just as my boss uttered his warning, I felt afraid. But I wasn't the only one; everyone in the street looked concerned. It felt like our lives were about to be overturned by a dragon of immense power.

April 1976: An act of defiance

The day of the Tomb-sweeping Ceremony

Less than a month later, in the early morning sunshine of April 5th 1976, father and I woke with a strange but powerful impulse. We made our way to Tiananmen Square and that impulse drove not just the two of us. We were not alone – a crowd began to gather – a crowd united by a common purpose. Beijingers had united to honour Zhou Enlai. We were there as individuals wanting to make a personal tribute to someone we respected but the individuals became hundreds, and the hundreds became thousands, then tens of thousands.

I don't know how it happened, Sara. There was no internet, no announcements, no notices in newspapers – all communications were controlled by the Gang of Four. Tiananmen Square is the biggest in the world and can hold one and a half million people. That day it was full!

Tension had been building ever since Zhou's death in January. Despite the Gang of Four not wanting any memorial to him, the people braved their wrath. Exhausted by the dreadful living conditions and without Zhou, they feared the situation would become even worse. Their grief for him was combined with wordless hatred of the Gang of Four. Thousands of people had risked imprisonment as they placed tributes to him in Tiananmen Square. I'd seen the results and wanted to show Ba.

As Father and I walked through the Gate of Heavenly Peace and down the tree-lined avenue towards the huge portrait of Chairman Mao, I hurried him along saying, 'Come and see; the white will dazzle you ...' but I couldn't believe the sight that greeted us.

'Ba, they're gone. Truly, yesterday the whole square was a sea of white. Where have all the tributes gone? What has happened to them?'

I glimpsed Weiwei and Jia not far ahead of us and rushed up to them.

'Weiwei, where are the wreaths?'

'The Gang gave orders for their removal. Overnight, the square was swept clear of every trace of white and they've banned the sale of white crepe.'

Sara, in China, white is the colour of mourning and white crepe is the material used to make tributes to the dead.

'Madame Mao is so arrogant she thinks she can sweep away the truth.' I sighed but I wasn't alone in that opinion. Looking around, I read the same thoughts on everyone's faces. So I forgot all the warnings, as did everyone else in the square that day. Around us the crowd was becoming angry and people were shouting at the soldiers guarding the Great Hall. China's supreme leaders were gathered there in the Great Hall of the People at the far end of this historic space. They would not like what they saw as the events unfolded outside.

More and more mourners passed us by, heading towards the monument in the middle of that immense space ... and they still kept coming ... and they were carrying little white flowers – flowers made from any kind of white paper not just the traditional crepe!

Word had got around of the clearing of Tiananmen Square, and thousands of people poured in carrying fresh wreaths and laid them around the memorial until the offerings grew into a small mountain. I watched as people threw paper blossom over the pine trees and smiled at the demonstrators around me who were wearing white paper flowers pinned to their Mao jackets.

Sara, we did not express our thoughts in words but we all read each other's minds. This spontaneous show of affection was for the dead premier. Whatever his mistakes and collaborations, they were all forgiven because he had tried his best to keep the country functioning while insanity and cruelty ruled.

The Gang of Four in the Great Hall of the People realized that the country was against them. I sensed that the mood around me had changed and some of the fear had gone. And the mourners kept coming in their hundreds of thousands, and laid flowers upon flowers around the Heroes Monument until it was almost invisible. And still they came until this immense space was overflowing with people. The vast square appeared blanketed with snow; everywhere was white, the colour of defiance. There was no need for words; there was an unspoken understanding that by demonstrating for Zhou we were demonstrating against the Gang of Four and their politics of conflict.

That day, we drew strength from each other. Four people held up a huge banner saying, 'We mourn the Premier'. Hundreds of people carried posters. Some had made life-size cut-outs of the dead prime minister and held them high. I watched as Weiwei took a shot at an acute angle to make one of them cover Mao's famous image at the apex of the monumental square.

'That's a fine angle.'

He replied,

'You understand what I mean.'

We were united. We did not need words but there were plenty of them. A young man, standing on a bike, read this poem and was almost drowned with cheers.

When I was going to cry
I heard the howling of the Devil
I am weeping while the wolf and jackal are laughing
I use my tears to honour the Great Soul
I open my eyes and pull my sword from its scabbard.

A howl of recognition arose from the crowd. Everyone knew whom he meant by the wolf and jackal.

The Forbidden City echoed with memories of a thousand years and everyone in Tiananmen Square knew that we were making history. We expressed ourselves in symbols and coded speech; but the dam of fear created by the Gang of Four had cracked. In cities around the country new slogans appeared: 'Deep-fry the persecutors of Premier Zhou!' The country was stirring from its downtrodden state and the atmosphere was liberating. The immense square vibrated with excitement but the Maoist establishment did not share our enthusiasm! For once the wolf and jackal were not laughing. Apparently, Madame Mao pointed her finger angrily at Mayor Wu De saying, 'This is counter-revolutionary,' insisting that Chairman Mao order the Mayor to deal with this abomination and act without delay to arrest those involved. In the square below, the mood was changing; someone set fire to a car outside the Civil Military Headquarters.

Mayor Wu De's voice echoed over the loud-speakers. 'This event is counter-revolutionary'.

Inside the Great Hall of the People, Madame Mao ordered Wu Zhong, the commander of the Beijing Military, to deploy his forces. He and Mayor Wu De knew what she meant but they didn't want bloodshed. Without doubt, they had friends amongst us. While the troops gathered, they tried desperately to procrastinate.

Over and over again, Mayor Wu De's voice repeated, 'Clear the Square. This event is counter-revolutionary.'

People were beginning to leave when behind us, the Civilian Military Headquarters in the east was suddenly engulfed in flames. Opposite, in the west, a huge setting sun coloured the sky gold and blood red.

Mayor Wu De's voice sounded loud and urgent. 'Leave the Square.'

Lines and lines of policemen and civil military were accumulating at an alarming rate. At the sound of marching, my father turned to me insisting, 'It is time to go – now!'

The red, yellow and gold vision before me was so vivid I couldn't drag myself away.

'I want to stay. I'll be all right; you go home, I'll stay with Jia and Weiwei', I said, but Father took me by the arm saying,

'You don't understand Chinese politics. We must go and go now.'

He spoke firmly to Weiwei and reluctantly, all four of us headed towards Chang An Avenue but I looked back over my shoulder to take in the dramatic scene. The fire consuming the military headquarters in the east seemed to reflect our anger against the authority of the Gang of Four and their denial of Zhou. Ahead hanging low in the sky was that beautiful blood red sunset and I let it warm my heart. This was a momentous day. Jia and I linked arms; it felt like an awakening, a fierce determination to bring about change. Rage and euphoria blended together as we made our way home.

Deng Xiaoping was dismissed from all his offices accused by the Gang of Four of organizing the demonstration. It had been just the excuse they had been waiting for. Mayor Wu De and Wu Zhong's tactics had saved lives but they couldn't prevent Madame Mao seeking her revenge. With cruel fury, she demanded the arrest of anyone who was in Tiananmen Square that day. Those unfortunate enough to be caught on camera were imprisoned. All factories, offices and schools were ordered to report anyone shedding tears for Zhou and to hand over demonstrators to the security forces. My boss was a good man. He was getting used to calling me into his office.

'Little Winter, I understand that you were just passing Tiananmen Square yesterday to deliver some work on Chang An Avenue. That's right isn't it?' I assured him that it was.

I was worried about Weiwei. Surely his bosses would know he was there, but even in the organ of the Communist Party establishment there were people like Mayor Wu De. Getting to the paper's headquarters in Chaoyang, a little to the north east of central Beijing, Weiwei could pass near Tiananmen. So he was asked no questions.

Mao's Lou Gehrig's disease had advanced and he was no longer able to speak intelligibly so he communicated by writing. A beaming Chairman Hua, Mao's nominal successor, was handed the message on a sheet of paper. *'Ni ban shi, wo fang xin'.* 'With you in charge, I feel at ease.'

News of Mao's speechlessness spread on the grapevine. The prospect of life after Mao with the Gang of Four in sole charge seemed a real possibility and filled us all with dread.

The Earth Speaks

Sara, after Nixon visited, learning English was permitted, so I was, at last, able to get a proper instruction book. Father had been disappointed with my progress using the dictionary but with Macmillan's 'Nine Hundred', learning English was easier and more fun. When you are annoyed with me, you mimic my accent. It is hard, almost impossible, to learn a new language as an adult, and speak it without an accent. It is my accent more than anything that makes me feel an outsider in this country.

The words in 'Nine Hundred' failed to impress me but the modern line-drawings depicting scenes of western life filled me with excitement. I was seeing another world and I let the style influence my illustrations for an instruction manual. It transformed a boring task at work. I showed it enthusiastically to Weiwei.

'I love this style don't you? It's so elegant.'

He wasn't impressed by my enthusiasm.

'You're getting excited over nothing. Sorry to say this but you work for a publishers, Snowdrop. Why don't you ask them to get you copies of western art books? Then you'll know what real artists are doing. These are just textbooks. Why don't you take yourself seriously?'

That day I left him in a huff, feeling quite hurt. But before I had the chance to take his advice, our world turned upside down.

Sara, living in San Francisco you understand earthquakes, but in California hardly anyone gets killed and most buildings are built to rock-and-roll. Even still, there have been plenty of times when the three of us have rushed out the door, so you will know the feeling I'm going to describe.

In the early hours of the morning of July 28th, I was awoken by an awesome sound: a dreadful deep rumble from the belly of the earth. Our building shook, the table trembled and our flower-pot fell to the floor sending earth flying in all directions. I hung on to the door and wedged it to prevent it jamming.

As the room swayed, I heard my mother's voice calling to me, urging me to action. 'Quick. Hurry. Get up! Earthquake.'

Suppressing the nausea arising in my stomach, I looked up and grew dizzy as I watched a crack spread across the ceiling. Dust and debris fell. Father was already dressed and pushed me out of the door before I had time to put on my jacket. He shouted,

'Get out now!'

He followed me down the concrete stairs, stepping over our neighbour's cabbages on the landing to the safety of the street and its commotion. In the crowds and noise, everyone was looking around anxiously as most houses were damaged. I told my father that I wanted to see if Jia and Weiwei and their family were okay and ran off down the road. My heart was pounding as a fearful picture of Weiwei lying dead under rubble formed in my mind.

The sun was mercilessly hot as Weiwei and I almost bumped into each other. He had had the same idea and was running at full speed to me. We skid to a stop and he seemed about to give me a hug, but then stopped short. There were so many people around ... it just wasn't done.

'Thank heavens, you aren't hurt. And your father?'

'He's fine but I don't think the flat is safe. How about yours?'

'The same. We have some water. Come and join us.'

Jia and her parents were trying to erect a temporary shelter from materials they had brought out of their apartment.

We waited for the aftershock. Expecting buildings to collapse, I headed back to my father. I didn't tell him about the strange experience in the morning – of how I heard my mother speak to me. We stood alongside our neighbours in the street until daybreak. I had plenty of time to think. I wondered if Weiwei's parents knew how Weiwei and I felt about each other. We had grown up like brother and sister but on this day, the thought of life without Weiwei was somehow unthinkable. I made a resolution. If we survived, we must be honest and tell them.

Father climbed over the dust and debris and brought out any material that could be of use. No sooner had he erected an awning than the heavens opened. Looking down the street, I felt so sorry for families with children trying to look after them in such miserable conditions. When at last the rain subsided, the pavements dried quickly in the heat. I spread a quilt on the ground and lay down. I could have slept for days but a few minutes later my neighbour was yelling at me.

'Xiaodong, come on, get up.'

The earth was trembling again. The humid heat, so hot: a haze lingered indolently over the pavements but the buildings stayed firm. Once again, I checked on Jia's family. I arrived just as Jia was leaving for the hospital.

'Why don't you come with me? You learned a lot in Manchuria; perhaps you can help.'

'I'd like to help but where is Weiwei?'

'They have sent him to Tangshan to take photos.'

August 20th 1976: Weiwei returns.

The casualties in Beijing had been mercifully few. The weather conditions and illnesses of the vulnerable living on the streets were the cause of most deaths. Three weeks passed before I saw Weiwei again. His kind round flat face appeared the same but his eyes seemed far away and his skin ash grey. His voice was dead. Weiwei could recite poetry with beauty but that day there was no expression in his words. Was this really my Weiwei? He suggested we walk to the North Sea Park where we sat by the lake soothed by the bamboo swaying gently in the breeze.

'Tell me about it, please,' I asked Weiwei proffering a packet of cigarettes.

I'm trying to remember when I started my filthy smoking habit, Sara. My first puff happened soon after Mother died and by 1976 it had become a serious habit. Weiwei and I used cigarettes to relax.

I knew there had been a massive earthquake in Tangshan but the news had reported that the brave miners had already returned to work.

'It wasn't like Beijing ...' began Weiwei.

'Tell me. Begin at the beginning.'

'In Tangshan, we tried to get off the train with our equipment but there was no station. As far as I could see, there was not a single building that wasn't damaged. I can't describe it. Have you heard of Hiroshima?' I nodded.

'It was like that,' he said.

'Why haven't they told us on the news?'

My parents had told me stories of unbelievable violence that took place after the Japanese invasion, and during the Civil War. I had seen traumatic incidents in 1967 but Weiwei's eyes had seen a horror that defied words.

'Xiaodong, we saw some bad things when the schools closed but nothing prepared me for what I have seen in Tangshan. Nothing – total destruction.'

Tangshan was the epicentre of the earthquake, Beijing was merely a ripple. The official figures for the dead was 242,000 and 164,000 injured, but in reality the death total was far higher. The unofficial estimate was 600,000 people killed. I couldn't understand why the government wanted to hide the true numbers of casualties. They couldn't be blamed for this because the cause was nature at its most terrifying.

Weiwei repeated the numbers of dead in an eerie voice that questioned sanity. I wasn't sure if it was meant to be his sanity or that of the world we inhabited.

'Our orders were to show how the words of Chairman Mao inspire the people with a determination to rebuild and recover. But they were too traumatised to do anything, Xiaodong. I clambered over the ruins with my camera but I was told not to dwell on the trauma but on the bravery of the people of Tangshan.'

I remembered what I had read in the papers and quoted it to Weiwei. 'Their first thoughts were for the motherland and restarting the mines even before they buried the dead.'

'Are we human or are we robots? I feel so ashamed. What good am I?'

I held Weiwei's hand tightly and leaned towards him. 'Surely your reports and pictures will have helped with the rescue operations?'

'The army was in charge. I saw ordinary soldiers working to the point of exhaustion, carrying body after body from the ruins. Oh Snowdrop ... the stench of death.'

I put my arms around him and held him tight. It was something I so wanted to do but I made sure no one was looking.

'The soldiers just kept going until they dropped but relief was slow coming and the reporters were not allowed to say that. We obeyed our orders, Xiaodong. I obeyed orders. Have I become some kind of robot?

'I met some miners emerging from the pits, soot-smeared from the night shift. First disbelief, then horror was etched on their worn faces. That morning, they had left their homes in the city to go underground. As they emerged in the twilight, they kept shutting their eyes in disbelief. Everything they knew had disappeared under rubble. I followed orders and photographed them but all they wanted to do was rush to find their loved ones.

'Wang tried to find words to express our concern for the victims but our overlords didn't print them or broadcast them. They say the priority is to denounce Deng. Can you believe it? You've read the paper. The picture they used does show the rubble but not the dead – not the image I sent. I stepped over bodies.'

Weiwei choked as he said it; his eyes looked vacant as if they had been drowned under bodies until they could see no more.

'As the editor trimmed my pictures, I expected a lecture; instead he looked embarrassed. Like me, he's just obeying orders.'

'What has the earthquake to do with Deng Xiaoping?' I asked.

'According to Madame Mao, Tangshan doesn't matter. She says, "There were merely several hundred thousand deaths. So what? Denouncing Deng Xiaoping concerns eight hundred million people." I asked myself, "What have we come to when a human life is of no consequence to our government?" '

His time in Tangshan had sucked the life force from Weiwei so I didn't get to tell him about my resolution. Somehow, what had seemed important – telling our parents about us – now seemed insignificant.

Bit by bit, I drew stories from him and the old Weiwei emerged from a distant place, shattered but at least feeling my presence.

He showed me some unedited pictures. It was horrifying even to look at them. I kept closing my eyes and turning away my gaze. I felt such a coward: it was too painful seeing the truth. In that moment, I understood why people don't like being faced with the truth. It digs deep inside you, disturbing your certainties about life. I thought we needed to be honest but I also felt relief that those terrible images weren't in the paper; they were so intense. They were among the best pictures Weiwei had ever taken but I couldn't look at them and they were never published. One of his stories I can never forget: it was about a young girl called Xiao Ping.

She had become wedged between two buildings. Her mother held her hand, stroked her forehead and spoke comforting words while soldiers tried desperately to rescue her. They worked for hours pulling out bricks and rubble by hand then suddenly they stopped; the lower part of her body was trapped between two huge concrete slabs – so large no human being could shift them by hand.

Sara, living in San Francisco, you have known about earthquakes and felt tremors since you were tiny. Our city is built to withstand shocks but we are prepared for the worst. You would say 'Set her free – bring in the heavy lifting equipment'. Even if they had a crane in Tangshan, there was no path through the mountains of debris.

Xiao Ping took fourteen days to die. In all that time, her mother stayed by her side holding her hand as they talked lovingly to each other. Offers of help had come from around the world and especially from here in the US but the Chinese government refused them all. How many people like Xiao Ping could have been saved if those offers had been accepted? But the government refused every one. They did not want foreigners poking around China. Weiwei's overlord, Yao Wenyuan, said, 'So what about the Tangshan earthquake? It only wiped a city off the map. Our main concern is for the revolution.'

Weiwei hesitated and in almost a whisper said, 'The smell, Xiaodong, you can't imagine the smell. It was gut wrenching, a putrid sickening stench. I keep washing and washing my face and nostrils over and over again but I can't get it out of my nose. I can still smell death on me even now.' He laid his head in his hands and sucked in breath then carried on. 'After ten days, they uncovered no more survivors. The dead had to be buried quickly to prevent disease. Body after body in mass graves.'

I wanted to comfort him but not go to the place he was in. Weiwei's mind could form questions when all around relied on parroting the answers we had been taught.

'Is this the value of an individual human life?' he whispered.

We had been taught that the individual was of no concern: 'The People' were all that mattered. Weiwei's question opened a chink in my mind. It made me ask a forbidden question. Who are the people? Aren't they individuals – all those dead people under the rubble? Once he started talking about it, he talked for hours.

'The water was polluted but somehow the sick and injured had to be cared for. Unfortunately, the shock had made casualties even among the survivors. We had to weave our way through people deranged by grief and traumatised by the horror of it all. But all our government cares about is continuing with coal production: to hell with the dead and dying!'

My worries about Weiwei intensified with his telling of the news. Our housing problems paled into insignificance. Gradually, my Weiwei emerged from the shell but exhaustion hung over him for weeks.

September 9th 1976: Our world turned upside down

At ten minutes past midnight, Chairman Mao's death was announced by the Central Committee of the Chinese Communist Party, the State Council, the Standing Committee of the National People's Congress and the party's Military Affairs Commission. His body was taken to lie in state at the Great Hall of the People.

Unlike with Zhou Enlai, there was no ignoring this one! You couldn't escape the obituaries and tributes, and a memorial service was planned for 18 September. As the news spread people rushed to buy or make black armbands. Crowds gathered opposite the huge portrait of Chairman Mao at the main entrance to the Forbidden City for a three minutes silence. The official Chinese obituary paid tribute to Chairman Mao's struggles against 'enemies' within the Chinese Communist Party! It was obvious who had chosen that sentence.

Obvious to us, Sara, but perhaps not to you. I'll explain it for you: Madame Mao and the Gang of Four wanted to seize complete and absolute power.

Fear's icy fingers gripped my heart. On the evening of the ninth, my father and I talked quietly at home about what could happen next.

'Ba, so many people are crying but I can't cry.'

'Please Little Winter, when you are out on the street, take a little wet dust and make your face look tear-stained. They are watching; anyone who doesn't cry is suspect. Be careful what you say.'

Ba leant so close to me our cheeks brushed as he whispered in my ear.

'This is possibly the most dangerous moment in your life. If the Gang of Four takes power, life in China will... We shall all live in fear all of the time. There are rumours of secret meetings at the Jade Spring Mountain. Some generals think that, if the Gang of Four seizes power, we shall have to fight again. I have seen one Civil War and I don't want to see another.' Ba gave a deep sigh.

Was the torment I had witnessed since 1966 just a flavour of worse to come? I wasn't the only person thinking that. The atmosphere in the office, the street, the shops and markets, everywhere was taut with fear and apprehension.

What has this to do with you, Sara? The next events changed China and eventually set it on the capitalist road to the China you see today. If everything had developed as Weiwei and I had hoped, I would not be here now and nor would you. Despite what was to come, Sara, I now know that it was worth it to have you.

Forgive me. I am critical of you too often. Young Americans are a mystery to me. Your language excludes me. When you called me 'wicked' today, I thought you meant that I was evil – that was why I was angry with you. Thank goodness that you have no idea what wicked truly is.

October 11th: We can breathe again

Weiwei met me coming out of the office. He made it look like a chance encounter then took me to the one place he thought it safe to talk, walking in the park. Other people we knew had suddenly decided to do the same thing. We waved to Weiwei's friend, Wei Jingsheng, who was talking eagerly with some of his friends. We sat in our favourite spot where the breeze rustled gently the thin bamboo beside the serene waters.

'Hua Guofeng has arrested the Gang of Four.'

'It's not funny, Weiwei. Please, don't tease me. Hua couldn't arrest them.'

'It is absolutely true and he wasn't alone. Snowdrop, we can breathe again.'

He stood up, stretched his arms, took a deep breath, then bent over to pick me up. He swung me round and round in joy. As I landed on my feet, he shielded me from view and kissed me. For once in my life I didn't worry about who could see us. With the Gang gone, we felt safe.

Sara, demonstrating affection in public is not the Chinese way and I felt uncomfortable about it. That is one thing I have found hard to adjust to in America.

I steadied myself and took a deep breath.

'Hero, do you really think there is a future for us?'

'Let things settle a bit and then I'll come and see your father.'

I don't think my face could have stretched into a wider smile and on that day, as the breeze rippled the bamboo, my heart echoed every little movement.

'Come on, we need to get a present for your father. Let's buy a bottle of wine.'

I had never seen such a huge queue at the shop before. After we bought our bottle of mao tai, the last few on the shelves soon disappeared into joyful hands. The news of the Gang of Four's arrest was not yet official but all the customers had heard on the grapevine. In America, I heard the phenomenon described as Chinese whispers and understood perfectly.

1977: Hope and joy!

I'll always remember the day Weiwei came to see my father. Ba took him into his study and closed the door on me. I paced around outside. My heart wouldn't keep still. It must only have been five minutes but it felt like hours of finger-wringing tension before the door opened and Ba came out beaming. He gave me a hug and that said it all. He liked Weiwei and Weiwei admired him. I felt so happy. Of course, nothing in China is that simple. We still had to be patient. Our work places and the Communist Party had to agree to our getting married. We needed a certificate from our employers. The government was even more concerned about the birth rate and had begun discussing a possible One–Child Policy. For the moment though, their response remained the same: discourage early marriage. The man should be twenty-seven and the woman twenty-five. I would soon be twenty-five but Weiwei was only nine months older than me. He could lose his job and not be given another one if we married without permission, so his father advised that we wait a year. It was hard but at least there was no secret about our relationship. I have no words for the joy we felt when Weiwei and I were able to meet frequently without Jia as chaperone or any pretence at just bumping into each other. We could show the world that we were meant to be together.

Because of the dramatic events there were plenty of foreign officials visiting Beijing. The city seemed to breathe more easily. Appearing too friendly with foreigners was dangerous but Weiwei now felt able to talk to members of the delegations he photographed. He told a cultural attaché from France about his artist friend and how I had been impressed with some book illustrations. That conversation had consequences: Weiwei came home bearing precious books. Each page revealed a new marvel. Before me were works by Monet, Cezanne, Renoir, Degas, Magritte, Dali and Van Gogh. Weiwei watched as I had my first exposure to modern Western art. I turned the pages of one book called, *The Impressionists.* I laughed.

'I heard the word Impressionism once before but used as an insult. It meant worthless capitalist art. But Weiwei, I can't explain why – the captured light – this art shines on me. Thank you. Thank you. I am going to study it hard. I have this feeling that these presents of yours will change my life.'

'I thought I had done that already,' grinned Weiwei, 'but obviously not enough.'

We were alone at the flat as my father was at an engineering conference. That night was the banquet for the delegates. Life was slowly becoming more about doing normal things instead of engaging in class warfare.

I felt happy and Weiwei radiated passion. His eyes were smiling again and he slowly explored my body, kissing every little bit of me. I seemed so weak. I, who had tried hard to be strong, had become a piece of wobbly jelly. Suddenly, Weiwei drew apart and ran to the bathroom. What had I done wrong? When he came back he looked as weak as I felt.

'Snowdrop, we must be careful until we are married. I'm sorry, I just don't know how I can wait that long.'

I thought he was going to cry. I held him close and told him not to worry.

'Maybe the wait will make it even sweeter?' He kissed me with the tip of his tongue.

Things began to change at work. Father explained that Deng Xiaoping was slowly gaining control of the government and wanted to reform the economy. He was looking optimistic for the first time since mother died and tried telling me about the engineering projects that he wanted to become involved with.

'We need to modernise. Some of us in the department are going to be allowed to visit Hong Kong. I would love to take you with me.'

Father did go: I was disappointed when I wasn't allowed to accompany him but he came back brimming with exotic tales of a city that was full to overflowing with people and ideas. He so enjoyed talking about it.

'The people are prosperous, Little Winter, not just the Westerners, the Chinese too. The press seems free – nothing hidden. Stories of the refugee camps, of strikes and of the Triads are there for anyone to read. The buildings are gleaming stalks growing higher and higher in search of light. And the streets, Little Winter, are filled with cars – the noise of the traffic is still echoing in my head. The engineers and scientists I met in the university all own cars. And they travel all over the world for conferences, where they discuss new ideas and techniques. That is Deng's vision for us, too, but it won't happen yet and I don't know how I can wait.

'I shouldn't talk like this. Hong Kong is also a colony, a symbol of our humiliation. When we had accommodation at the Summer Palace, it made me angry to know that foreign troops had stormed it, looted it and destroyed so much of it. The destruction was painful but the knowledge of our weakness was even more painful.'

I put a plate of spring rolls on the table and offered them to Ba. As he began to eat he said,

'And the food – Xiaodong – I have never eaten so well. And the clothes – we looked like shabby country yokels. Which reminds me – I have bought you a present.'

Ba went into his study and came back with a parcel wrapped in silver starred paper and tied with red ribbon. It looked so perfect that I didn't want to spoil it.

'Silly girl, open it. Open it.'

I did but slowly, relishing every fold. Beneath was a smooth cream box embossed with gold letters in English and Chinese. I took off the lid and lifted the delicate tissue paper to see a western wedding dress. I fingered the cream silk with disbelief. It was beautiful to touch. I carefully laid it on the table. Around the neck and the sleeves were embroidered tiny pearls. Attached to the back of the dress from the bra line flowed a train.

'Aren't you going to put it on?' urged Ba.

'It's too lovely to wear. Look at me.' And I began to cry.

'What do you mean, Little Winter? You are as pure and lovely as Manchurian snow. Your Weiwei is a lucky man. Do as you are told. You are still living in your father's house and I want you to put it on.'

I took it into my room but changed into clean underwear before trying it. There was a zip at the side carefully hidden. I slid it up centimetre by centimetre feeling the fabric gradually moulding itself to my body.

'What are you doing in there? I've never known you take so long.'

Father stopped talking as soon as I opened the door and walked towards him. He looked as if he was about cry.

'My daughter, you look like a film star. Better still, you look like your mother would have looked in that dress when we married.'

'But Ba, don't let anyone hear you say that. You know people will be jealous. It is so lovely. If only I could wear it for our wedding but it's capitalist. Just imagine the condemnation.'

'Things are changing, Xiaodong, but you are right. It is best not to wear it to the civil ceremony but you can to the banquet. I know just the place. They have a private function room and you will be able to change into it there. Has your certificate been signed?'

It took another three months before Weiwei received his letter giving us permission. That took us into 1978, but in the spring we were to be married. It was not easy to find accommodation in Beijing and to begin with Weiwei was going to move in with us. Although the walls were thin between the rooms, our flat was big enough, partially because Father's study was also his bedroom. Of course, I had dreams of one day having a home of our own but in the interim, while Ba still lived, I at least knew he would never be lonely. There had been comments when Ma died that we should move out and let a large family have our apartment, but somehow we were lucky and it never happened. Perhaps we were saved because Father often brought home engineers, seconded from the provinces, to live with us for a few weeks at a time.

So my room would soon be our room. I kept pinching myself. I couldn't believe it. I scrubbed every inch of our room removing each speckle of Beijing dust. Ba arranged for some western emulsion paint to be sent from Hong Kong. There was a lot of curiosity when it was delivered. It had obviously been opened by security but they had passed it. Soon the walls looked as fresh as a vase of lilies. I had saved enough money to buy new sheets. I embroidered covers for our pillows and sewed a new cover for our quilt.

When I proudly showed it to Weiwei, I was upset when he said, 'You've missed the most important thing.'

'But I thought you would like it.'

'Of course I like it, but where is the picture?'

'Which picture?'

'Snowdrop, I tell everyone that I am marrying an artist and yet there is not a single picture painted by you on the wall.'

'I promise there will be one. Do you think it will be safe if I paint like an Impressionist?'

I took out one of my precious books and showed him Monet's lily pond.

'Don't you just love those watery colours. They suit your name, Weiwei. What do you think? Water and purple bamboo flowing in Monet colours? Will I be arrested, do you think?'

'We shall hang it on this wall so no unfriendly eyes can see it, and your father's not going to tell anyone.'

'I am so lucky. I must have been fifteen before I realised that. I thought all fathers were like mine. How stupid of me. You're right. Ba will say he loves it even if he thinks it's the worst painting I have ever done and he won't criticise me because it doesn't have heroes and heroines in it. He loves woodcuts and I don't think he likes these foreign pictures. I remember when you gave me this book, I almost cried I was so excited. I showed it to Ba but he said, "If you say so, then it must be good."'

'You know how much I admire your father, you do, don't you Snowdrop? We are going to be very happy.'

During the month leading up to our wedding, I set to work on a big canvas. After buying it and the paints, I had hardly any savings left. That was very un-Chinese. Because of disasters, human and natural, we are avid savers. I was anxious as I made the first brush stroke. I had not worked on such a big picture since the posters of the Cultural Revolution but they were bold calligraphy and mostly black and white and they didn't involve me. This picture was personal; so quite daring and dangerous. Each colour was significant. I suddenly felt nervous and afraid. It was a dreadful failure. I couldn't do it.

Father came home to find me in tears.

'What do you mean, you can't paint? I have watched you paint and draw since you were two.'

'This is different. I always knew what to do. I had to do what was expected of me. I feel empty, Ba. Who am I? These brush strokes will be free. They will express me, who I am, and suddenly I don't know.'

'What do you mean, you don't know who you are? I have never heard such nonsense. You are my daughter. You are your mother's daughter. I expect this is wedding nerves. Oh Little Winter, if your mother were here, she would know what to say but there's only me.'

I hated making him look sad. So the next day, I came home more determined and mixed a pale green and splashed the paint almost irritably on the canvas. Then I stood back and laughed. I liked it. I actually liked it. Again and again, I stippled and swept and let the shades run into each other like water. Yes, that was what I wanted. I wanted Weiwei and me to be like that; to flow in and out of each other like the tides. I had once seen the sea. Father had been born in Dalian, a port in Liaoning Province. He took me there to see grandmother before she came to live with us. I loved the sea. It looked like an enormous canvas. Every ripple a brush stroke; I wanted it to feel textured but laughed as it dissolved to the touch.

Father helped me hang the picture on the wall. 'You'll need a boat,' he joked.

It was to be a surprise wedding present from me. I hoped Weiwei wouldn't laugh at it.

Part 3: ART AND LOVE

Together at last

I'll never forget Weiwei's face when I walked into the restaurant wearing my western wedding dress. He couldn't take his eyes off me; he looked so proud. As I sat beside him, he whispered softly in my ear, so softly that, with the general buzz, I hoped Ba didn't hear. But a blush spread over my face and I looked quickly down and covered my face as he said,

'You're as soft as the first snows of winter. I'm so hungry; I want to lick every inch of you. Now it's legal ... I want all of you, every little tiny bit of you ...'

The banquet began, served in the traditional way. Fifty dishes, one for each of our guests plus one extra. When the wine was poured, Weiwei made an old-fashioned gesture. He filled both our bowls and asked me to sip a little from mine while he drank from his. Then he mixed together the remaining wine from both our bowls into one bowl and we both drank from it.

'Now everyone knows that we are one – one life flowing into the other.'

There was no honeymoon. We both had to be at work on Monday but our room was like a cocoon. Weiwei adored the painting and adored me and my hero was lying next to me. We spent the whole of Sunday exploring each other. Weiwei mapped every nook and crevasse of my universe until the demon in me was released in a dreadful frenzy. This wild being within me that had lain hidden for so long was set free. When I lay back, exhausted, from some distant world came the subtle warmth of Weiwei's voice.

'Here is wintery Harbin,' as he stroked my forehead, 'and these mounds of spice are ...' moving one finger around my little breasts, 'exactly here is the warm South, and here is the humid island of Hainan.'

Was there a luckier girl in all of China?

Taking new steps

As I woke each day to my new life as a wife, I repeated the word over and over to convince myself that we were married. The people of Beijing were doing a similar thing. They were trying new things and then waiting for the heavens to fall in and couldn't quite believe it when they didn't. In November, sixteen teachers at the No 2 Foreign Languages Institute published 1500 poems. Many of those poems were ones I had heard in Tiananmen Square on Tomb-sweeping Day in 1976: poems commemorating Zhou Enlai, others like the howling against the jackal and the wolf. These poems had been illegal and led to incarceration and even death for many, so I stared unbelieving at the book in my hand, yet no one came to arrest me. I opened it and there was a dedication by none other than the premier, Hua Guofeng. I startled Weiwei with a loud gasp of surprise.

'Hero, am I getting old? Do I remember it correctly? Hua did send in the troops that day, didn't he? He called the gathering counter-revolutionary.'

'That's politics, Snowdrop. Politicians sway with the wind. Deng is influential again, so now it was a completely revolutionary event. You can understand why the poets are not happy about Hua's inscription, but there is nothing they can do about it.'

I was pleased because it meant there was a thaw. A distant aroma of freedom was in the air and we held our breath in case we blew it away. In my imagination, I opened a window on a dream to be an openly free artist, just as I could openly love Weiwei. Happiness seemed just beyond my grasp but not a crazy impossible dream.

Ba was right in his prediction. I was twenty-four years old when I went to university to learn English properly. There was going to be a lot of work translating foreign texts and, if I mastered the language, I could have a job doing that. I felt excited about the prospect until I realised that most would be technical books. Still, if I could read and get hold of the kind of books I wanted, there would be no stopping me learning about the world beyond China.

1978-79: The Stars Movement

Sara, the China you see today was the creation of Deng Xiaoping. It was at this time that he took control of the economy and began a step-by-step liberalisation. Deng's first steps up the capitalist road were of course opposed by the Maoist faction. He worked out a strategy to outwit them.

I remember the day when Weiwei burst through the door; he was so excited. In fact I thought he would explode. It wasn't the loosening of the economic stays that had sent him into a tizzy but the possibility of having a voice that enthralled him.

'Snowdrop, I must take you to Xidan. It's a miracle.'

'Slow down, Hero, what is this miracle?'

'The Democracy Wall? Can you believe it? Deng has allowed a Democracy Wall! People are writing complaints about corrupt officials on it and not being arrested.'

My cynical Weiwei started to dance but not well – so I laughed. At the sound of my laughter, his feet came to an abrupt halt as a shade of doubt spread over his face.

'I don't know if I dare believe it. Do you think this is the same kind of trick Mao played? Let people feel free to speak so you know your enemies and then destroy them.'

I could see that he had convinced himself; he looked so deflated. I tried to cheer him up saying,

'I found some hot chillies in the market today and tonight your restaurant is serving the finest Szechuan chicken. That will put fire in your belly.'

And Sara, I shouldn't describe what I did but one day soon you will know.

Weiwei was taken by surprise and gasped, 'You're so good for me, Snowdrop. I love coming home to you.'

When Ba arrived home, we sat together to enjoy the meal. He had also heard about the Democracy Wall and opened a celebratory bottle of wine.

'How long do you think it will last?' asked Weiwei.

'Deng suffered as much as anyone during the madness. You know his son was paralysed when he was forced to jump out a window of a block of flats? Deng wants us to join the world and not be so inward-looking. As long as he is not taking the cork out of the bottle so suddenly that people get silly, as long as things are allowed to change gradually, we have reason to hope.'

Weiwei nodded and said, 'I'd like your advice. Wei Jingsheng has started an underground magazine called Exploration and he says Jiang He – you know the poet – is writing for a magazine called *Today*. They meet in an old courtyard house owned by Zhao Nan down a narrow houtong in east Beijing. I bumped into Jingsheng and he took me to a gathering.'

Weiwei described how strange and exciting it felt because the talk that rebounded off those ancient timbers was of dangerous political ideas.

'Writers for *Peking Spring* were discussing the work of one of the editors, Bei Dao. That's why I got carried away when I saw the Democracy Wall. These people are writing on it. I really want to join them, I want to write from the heart but with my background do you think I'll damage them?'

Weiwei looked anxiously at Ba, who wasn't able to dismiss his fears. Ba replied, 'Son, once the Security Bureau have their claws into someone, they never really let go. I'm sorry but I can see that you know this. You were imprisoned during the madness but that won't harm you as long as you don't get involved in politics. But if you do, they will definitely close in on you. They will have planted someone – they have ears everywhere.'

Seeing Weiwei's downcast look I said, 'I'd love to see a copy of *Today*. That'll be okay, won't it? Let's be involved by reading it.'

That cheered him up a bit and when we were alone that night, he said, 'We're lucky being able to talk frankly like this. It's not common; you do know that, Snowdrop? Your father is wise but is also positive: I like his attitude. I hope I can be like him. It's just that I want to be more than a newspaper photographer.'

'The atmosphere is changing. One day you may be able to throw away those small shoes and be free do what you want. But I think Ba is right. That may happen sooner if you don't get involved in politics.'

The next day, I managed to get a copy of Today from a friend in the office. There was a poem in it, by Bei Dao, which was so different that I wasn't sure that I understood it. It was called Huida (The Answer)

I come into this world
Bringing only paper, rope, a shadow.

Sara, the word 'shadow' was taken up by critics and they called this kind of verse 'poetry of shadows'. Bei Dao was exiled but he was allowed to return to work in China in 2006, maybe because he was nominated for the Nobel Prize in Literature.

He married Shao Feng, the skater from Red Women's Army on Ice. Today *is the only magazine started in that volcanic era which still survives.*

I felt even more excited when I held the next edition because it included illustrations and the cover was different – so attractive. I read a poem by Jiang He, whose name means river.

English names don't have the same resonance for me. Sorry Sara, you'll think I'm such a hypocrite not giving you a Chinese name. Sometimes when you rebel against me – I try to think of how I felt repressed and wanted to be free. You must flow free and I must stop trying to dam you up.

Jiang He's poetry was like his name; it flowed, flowed beautifully. This poem was different – like nothing I had read before. He titled it Unfinished Poem.

Black Time gathered, like a crowd of crows.
From every corner of the world,
from every night of History,
To peck all the heroes to death, one after the other,
The Agony of the heroes thus became a rock,
Lonelier than mountains.
For Chiselling and sculpting,
The Character of the nation,
Heroes were nailed to death.
Wind-eroding, rain-beating,
An un-certain image revealed upon the wall –
Dismembered arms, hands and faces –
Whips slashing, darkness pecking,
Ancestors and brothers with heavy hands,
Laboured silently as they were piled into the wall.
Once again I come here.
To revolt against fettered fate,
And with violent death to shake down the earth
From the wall
To let those who died silently stand up and cry out

It was horrible yet wonderful. It had such courage and the illustration by Lu Shi was full of humanity, not a stereotypical impression of the masses but instead the emotion of a brave woman. The artist was obviously Chinese but the style was fresh and original. How I yearned to meet the poet and the artist. When I did, I discovered that Lu Shi was the pen name of Qu Leilei. Weiwei and I discussed the poem that night and needed to know more. There was something we were missing but what?

Sara, The underground magazines and the Democracy Wall were my windows on freedom of speech and it loomed large in my life during its brief two-year existence. I went there every week. It was like I had to pinch myself that it was really happening. People came from all parts of the country to paste stories about torture and corrupt officials in the hope of finding justice.

In December, I watched as Weiwei's friend, Wei Jingsheng, pasted a *dàzìbào*, a large character poster, called Democracy: The Fifth Modernisation. Wei Jingsheng was so clever. I struggled with his ideas but my instinct told me he was right. Democratic participation was what we wanted, a say in how the country of our birth was run. But how? How does a country the size of China, which has been controlled from the centre for two thousand years, embrace a democratic system? At the Democracy Wall I was swept up by the dream of it. I was filled with passion but I had no answers.

A few days later, Weiwei rushed into the flat looking anxious and agitated. He paced up and down the room with clenched fists but said nothing. My head throbbed; I tried to take his hands but he covered his eyes with them. It probably was only minutes but it felt like hours. I pleaded with him.

'What is the matter? Sit down, pleeease. Tell me.'

He took a deep breath then sat down with his head in his hands. He looked up with wide watery eyes.

'They've arrested Wei Jingsheng.'

'Why, what's he done?'

'You told me about it, Xiaodong – his *dàzìbào*! Deng Xiaoping has taken it personally. From now on, who can write freely anymore? It's over. I thought this time was different. You remember Deng said the Democracy Wall should continue forever. Turns out, forever was two years.'

Before me was a despairing, frustrated man. Since we'd been married, the future was a place we wanted to visit. I didn't want to lose my optimistic Weiwei. What could I do to bring him back?

'Let's go to Zhao Nan's and see what they think.' I suggested.

He agreed and that evening changed my life. Weiwei recognised the democracy activists Lu Qing and Xu Wenli, close friends of Wei Jingsheng and went over to talk to them, anxiety etched on his broad face.

I felt guilty because for me there was delight – the place was buzzing with artists and these artists expressed what I desired for my art; they were putting into words my half-formed ideas. There was Ma Desheng, Wang Keping, Qu Leilei, Huang Rui, A Cheng and another Weiwei – Ai Weiwei; so many now famous names. In the gloom, through a haze of cigarette smoke, they were discussing putting on a show of ground-breaking new art. Spell-bound, I listened as they discussed what to call themselves.

Names seemed to fly around the room but none seemed to capture the zeitgeist until Wang Keping said "Xingxing' (The Stars). Everyone loved it: it had so many interpretations. Stars look small in the sky but are actually bigger than the sun. In Mandarin, the symbol also means spark and they wanted to be sparks that light a fire. So they became The Stars or at least hoped to be.

They'd tried to get an official exhibition in the National Art Gallery but were refused. Despite that, they were determined to abandon propaganda art and try new things. And the joy of it! The Stars wanted to recruit other artists to join them. My mind tingled with excitement but I was quite shy and this was my first time meeting them.

On the way home I asked Weiwei, 'Should I tell them I'm an artist? They'll be embarrassed by the work I do. It's the kind of art they want to escape. But I do too, Weiwei. You know how I long to experiment. Dare I tell them?'

'How strong is your desire? If you want to express yourself so much that you can't live without it, then you should join them. Otherwise forget it. Wei Jingsheng's in prison, Snowdrop – I know what that's like – I don't want you to know. It could be dangerous.'

'I haven't felt like this before, Hero. I want to light the fire inside me but what if I can't produce anything good?'

'You know that if The Party doesn't like your independent spirit and want to put you in jail, there is nothing to stop them. But you have my support whatever you decide.'

I made my decision and became a regular visitor at Zhao Nang's bohemian house. The walls were cracked and stained. The meeting room was lit by a single bare bulb but the atmosphere was electrically charged. Every square inch was occupied and almost everyone was smoking cigarettes. And it was there that I met the poet, Jiang He, and learned the story behind his poem. It was the story of a heroine but a different kind compared with those I had learned about in school.

Sara, you are seeing the story beneath my skin. I hope you will discover me as you peel back my layers of memory but sometimes I don't want you to know. Knowledge changes people. You have everything to look forward to, to be optimistic about, to believe in the goodness of people.

I believe that was the night I started to understand myself and to think freely. Weiwei had been able to do that for a long time but I didn't have his depths. Weiwei's warning to me was not exaggerated. The heroine behind Jiang He's poem was Zhang Zhixin. In 1969, Zhang had dared to criticize Mao Zedong's ideology, the Cultural Revolution. They put her in a tiny cell for a year and a half. It was so small she could not stand straight or sit down with her feet stretched out. In 1975, after six years in jail they released her for execution, first cutting her throat so no one could hear her opinions.

When Jiang He told me that story I didn't really want to believe it but knew it was true. The problem is when you know the truth, it changes you. In America, I learned the Bible story about Adam and Eve in the Garden of Eden. They ate from the Tree of Knowledge and their life was never the same again. I was like that.

On my next visit, the mood was gloomy and depressed. Wang Keping reported back from the National Gallery.

'The answer is NO! They say there are no vacancies for other exhibitions.'

The economy and industry were beginning to change direction but art was still Maoist; individual expression was forbidden. We had been taught that art should serve the masses – that is the workers, peasants and soldiers – the 'clean' elements in society. But, at Zhao Nang's house, there were no masses, only talented individuals who wanted to express themselves. They didn't seek revolution but the establishment would not give an inch. A Cheng suggested that The Stars approach the Beijing Artists Association one last time and attempt to book a date in the future, even for 1980. Persistence revealed the truth; their refusal had nothing whatsoever to do with timing but everything to with content. They rejected The Stars' ideas as too radical.

Ma Desheng was full of vitality and consumed by righteous anger, he rocked the room when he suggested mounting an unofficial exhibition. At least, it sounded like him but the room was gloomy even if the atmosphere sparkled. The light of that single light bulb cast people into shadow like Bei

Dao's poetry and everyone seemed to be talking at once. The decision of the ten leaders was foolhardy; they were willing to plan an illegal exhibition and risk arrest. Comradeship and mutual support banished fear; they looked invincible. By this time, even I had plucked up courage to show them some of my work and felt like floating into space myself when they liked it. But I knew I hadn't the courage of Zhang Zhixin, so I would need to steel myself to take part.

At the next meeting, The Stars discussed the practicalities. They struggled to come up with a venue. Where could they hold it? Someone suggested the Democracy Wall but Huang Rui thought that too political. Qu Leilei suggested the big wall outside the Television Studios.

'Since I work there, I could keep an eye on it.'

But the others felt that was too far from the centre. Silence. Then it dawned on everyone, almost simultaneously,

'We're not allowed inside. But no one has said we can't be outside the National Gallery!'

It was a Eureka moment. The gallery was in the centre of Beijing and to the right of it was a small park. A high fence ran between the gallery and the park. What a temptation for a group of enterprising young artists! We could all visualise our paintings hanging on that fence and the vision of one of my pictures hanging there banished my fear. Life with Weiwei had brought contentment but this was something beyond dreams. I knew that this illegal exhibition was going to change my life but couldn't even imagine how.

We had a venue so all that was needed was a date. Someone, I can't remember who, suggested October 1.

Sara, October 1st is National Day when China celebrates the beginning of the People's Republic and it is a public holiday.

Beijingers would be out and about and have time to see it. It was agreed and everyone began to prepare. At the final planning meeting, the discussion was about how many works we should exhibit and then someone said, 'Isn't it provocative setting up on National Day itself? Why don't we begin earlier in the week?'

That was how 7:00 am on the 27th September was cast as the launch date of the first contemporary art show in China! A lot of the artists stored their work in Qu Leilei's flat. Dare I show one of mine? That night I could hardly stop talking about it.

Weiwei asked 'You are going to tell me which of your paintings you will exhibit? I presume that is what this excitement is all about?'

'I so want to be part of it but mine aren't good enough.'

'You know why I call you Snowdrop? You are beautiful and perfect but you don't believe it. You hide your talent in the undergrowth. I'm scared for you... but that is ridiculous; you are every bit as good as the other Stars.'

When he realised that I longed to take part, Weiwei took the initiative. He secretly selected one of mine and added it to the pile! He picked the right one because I learned that the founders vetted potential exhibits and had only accepted work they considered radical. I had been experimenting and Weiwei took a semi-abstract painting. I had titled it Transition to Spring and it had cold colours becoming warmer colours. It could have many interpretations.

I was so pleased he did that for me as I am not sure that I would ever have felt my art worthy. When the Stars chose my painting, I had an awesome premonition. Our paintings would not be in a prestigious gallery: they were to be hung on railings but a strange certainty filled my being. We were changing the history of Chinese Art and Weiwei's generous gesture would change my life. From now on I would call myself an artist.

Word had spread even before our posters appeared on the Democracy Wall, around the University and in Today magazine. The grapevine was as effective as jungle drums.

The Stars shine

Sara, Ai Weiwei designed the Bird's Nest stadium for the Olympic Games. It is extraordinary. As I write this part of my memoir, I have just received a letter with sunflower seeds from Sylvia in England. Do you remember her? She came to my last show. Anyway, Ai Weiwei has an installation in the Turbine Hall at Tate Modern in London. It's a great honour – he's only the eleventh artist to be given that vast space. He's covered it with one hundred million sunflower seeds – except they are not sunflower seeds, but individually made porcelain copies. They are like human beings; we have a common form but each one of us is unique.

Holding one sunflower seed, I can picture the young Ai Weiwei looking directly at me on that historic day in 1979 as we transported our work with great reverence on tricycles! I don't know how but they arrived undamaged and amazingly; we had taken the authorities by surprise. Using plenty of wire to attach our work to the railings outside the National Gallery, the hanging took almost two hours. My heart raced but no one stopped us.

Crowds began to gather and the ones at the back could see nothing. We took some ropes and tied them between trees, to mark out a pathway. It was surreal seeing people queuing in such an orderly manner in that makeshift open-air gallery.

Sara, I didn't even know the word 'surreal' then; now I love the word. And the concept. And the art that reflects it.

The photographer Wang Ju Ching arrived to record the exhibition. I felt as if I had swallowed a growth medicine; I swelled with pride seeing my painting inspired by Monet, alongside the sensational work of the twenty others.

Qu Leilei's pictures were chosen to be first and his opening shot was a symbol of freedom, a nude figure leaping into the air.

Sara, to you that must sound tame. It's your strange mother getting excited about nothing. There have been nudes in Western art since the Renaissance, but in China they were almost unheard of in public art. It was sensational!

It was very shocking. Weiwei came to see the show and was so moved by the black and white drawings that he kept getting in the queue and going round again and again. He learned that Qu Leilei had been in Tangshan with China TV. He had seen what Weiwei had seen and sketched spontaneously. He called one of them The Girl with the Tear Drop. It expressed emotion and contained a spirit that a photograph could not. Weiwei had seen the source of her tear and wished it could become a river to wash away the visions that disturbed him in the middle of the night.

Ma Desheng's prints were powerful woodcuts. One showed a Chinese peasant driving his wooden plough across the chest of a sleeping man. They were about the clean groups the government wanted art to represent but they were not socialist realism, they were humanism.

Wang Keping posted a set of questions and answers at the entrance to the exhibition.

Q. What is this sculpture about? I can't tell what it's meant to be.

A. It is itself. It doesn't have to be something else in order to be worthwhile.

Q. I can't understand this picture. All I can see are some colours leaping about.

A. You have understood it correctly.

Except that I didn't really understand, not really. That I do now is down to your father, Sara.

Wang Keping's work was ironic but in 1979, I didn't really understand 'irony'. He carved a provocative 'Fist,' a wooden bust of a man with a giant hand strapped over his mouth. Huang Rui's were vivid semi-abstracts paintings. Ignorant though I was, I felt delight seeing something that may not actually mean anything concrete.

Can you understand that, Sara?

Yan Li expressed emotion and personal imagery: something almost unknown in China. A Cheng's was a moving portrait of Zhou Enlai whereas Bo Yun's paintings had the soul of Daoism.

Sara, Daoism is an early Chinese philosophy. Its founder LaoTsu thought we should walk with nature and his ideas influenced art, particularly the importance of empty space, the void.

In 1969, to paint traditional landscape was dangerous but in 1979, the atmosphere was different. I can't find words to explain what it felt like to see Transition to Spring hanging next to the National Gallery. I felt like caterpillar turning into a butterfly.

I am sorry, Sara, I wish I had it to give to you but I arrived in San Francisco almost empty handed.

The effect of our work hung together was quite startling. We had been starved of the spirit of Lao Tsu. Our imaginations had been fed propaganda paintings of Mao and heroic workers. Bo Yun echoed all our feelings when he said, 'I feel so happy. For the first time, I am painting as a true artist.'

That didn't stop me being nervous. Don't forget we had only recently been exposed to Western art, so what would visitors make of the show? How would they react? Would they be shocked?

All our friends came. Father supported the exhibition and arranged to meet lots of comrades there and they were a sympathetic audience. Our visitors' book showed almost a thousand came on the first day. Qu Leilei's father was one of the thousand who signed it. It was only then that I realised that Leilei was the son of Qu Bo, one of our most popular novelists. Madame Mao had taken a section from his *Tracks in the Snowy Mountains* and turned it into one of her model operas. Half of the population of China knew and loved his books and he had looked at my picture!

On the next day, the 28th, the crowds kept coming but this time none of them knew us. Word had got around and curiosity brought them. Our edginess cooled when their reaction was not hostile but enthusiastic: they were bored by the bland sameness of illustration that was approved by party culture. Our happiness and optimism knew no bounds. When officials in the National Gallery saw that the reaction was friendly, some plucked up courage and gave their support. They allowed us to store our paintings inside overnight.

I arrived a little late on the 29th because of a meeting in the office and immediately realised that something had changed, changed utterly.

Shao Fei and I knew each other from The Red Women's Army on Ice. I ran towards her and bombarded her with questions. 'What's happened? Where are they?' I looked towards the mass of policemen and asked, 'Have they taken them?' Several Stars answered at the same time.

'When we arrived the entrance to the storeroom was blocked by thirty policemen and then even more officers formed a circle around us.'

I saw The Stars looking despondent standing around in groups on the paved area near the fence where only the day before visitors stood to admire our work and leave talking excitedly about what they had seen. I think most of us were a little afraid but were trying hard not to show it. Everyone tried not to notice that the others were hiding their feelings.

Suddenly Qu Leilei walked up to the police and said, 'Why are you stopping us getting in?'

All the while, people were arriving to see the show. A policeman answered Leilei in a non-threatening manner. 'You are obstructing the traffic.'

Ma Desheng looked around and pointing to the road said, 'This is a public park and its twenty metres from the road!'

The police spokesman seemed lost for words so Wang Keping took advantage of the moment hesitation to ask, 'Do you think there is anything wrong with our paintings?'

The officer in charge took ages before he tried to answer and eventually stuttered, 'Uh ... the masses have had some reactions to your paintings.'

Quite a crowd had gathered around us and we were excited when some of them chimed in. 'We're the masses, too, and we think their exhibition is great.'

For the first time that morning, I smiled but the enthusiastic crowd provoked another officer who stepped forward looking impatient and annoyed. 'Your exhibition is interfering with other people's activities.'

I gasped as Wang answered him sounding confident and unafraid. 'We're enriching their cultural life. We are making a contribution to National Day.'

While we talked the crowd had grown even bigger making the police feel uneasy and agitated.

Ma Desheng had suffered from polio as a child, and as a result was on crutches. Thinking he looked less threatening, the five founders of the Stars pushed him to the front to talk to them. It was a mistake: Ma was quick-tempered and started to shout angrily. The police looked at Qu Leilei because, with his broad calm face, he looked rather serene. They asked his name and he told them and then he tried to talk 'art' but they talked 'security'.

The five founders gathered together to discuss what to do. They knew that the decision to block the exhibition was made by bureaucracy higher up the chain of command, and these officers had no choice but to enforce it. So Wang Keping and Qu Leilei were dispatched to attempt to resolve the situation at the Security Bureau! I was impressed. They cycled to the Eastern City Branch while we hung around not knowing what to do. The police seemed to relax so we all relaxed. I sat on the ground leaning up against the fence and waited.

I waved when the two pedalled into view. In seconds we circled them, eager to know what happened and relieved that they seemed unfazed.

Qu Leilei described how they asked the officers at the Security Bureau,

'Why use so many police to surround a group of peaceful artists? In what way is our exhibition illegal?'

When they failed to get answers to these questions, Wang Keping suggested trying the nearby High Court. He knew a judge who worked there and explained the situation to her. After listening to their description of the events, she sounded sympathetic so they asked, 'Is there anything wrong with showing our work in the park?'

She couldn't see anything wrong, so they asked again, 'So why did the police stop us? Had they the right to stop us?'

Her equivocal response gave them confidence.

'Can we ask the court to recommend that the Security Bureau allow us to re-open the exhibition either inside or outside?'

Grinning, Wang made an audacious request. 'Can we sue them?'

It was question after question that day. That was something new: the freedom not just to resist what our leaders told us, but also to question it.

The idea of a bunch of artists suing the Beijing Security Bureau amused the judge but, despite her smiles, the outcome was not in doubt. While they were telling us all this, Chi Xiaoning, from the Film Academy was ordered to stop filming by two policemen. It was late afternoon and everything seemed to be grinding to an unsatisfactory halt when someone suggested an emergency meeting.

The obvious venue was Zhao Nan's house. The word spread like lightening and as well as the Stars, the place was crowded with members of *Today* and of *Peking Spring*. Anyone remotely involved in the new thinking wanted to be there. The room used for most meetings was not large enough so we gathered in the courtyard. Some stood, others sat on the benches and chairs scattered around until it was full to overflowing. I looked through the thick cigarette smoke as Hao Nan opened the meeting.

In politics we want democracy and in art we want freedom

The atmosphere was emotional and agitated but everyone became quiet and listened intently as Liu Qing and Xu WenLi, two democracy activists who edited a journal called Fifth April Forum, came forward to chair the gathering. A solemn Liu told us, 'We are facing a new and rare opportunity. If there is to be a "war", this is one we win.'

Xu Wenli nodded in agreement.

'The Stars' exhibition was a great success and was not illegal. What was illegal was the action of the East Beijing Security Bureau in sending police to close it down.'

Wang and Leilei described how they had asked the Beijing Authority to reopen the show either outside or inside the Gallery. Liu said 'We will give the Beijing Authority one day to make a decision.'

The temperature of the meeting rose to fever pitch. National Day is October 1st and this was early evening on September 29th. Zhao made a Chinese joke to lessen the tension.

'If the Mayor had two heads, neither of them would want anything to mar the celebrations. That is why we have just one day to prepare our response,' he said.

The discussion continued for a while before the meeting agreed to write a final notice to the Beijing Authority. Liu suggested that we put in writing what Wang and Leilei had asked them but suggested adding that if they deny us the opportunity to exhibit our work, we will meet on National Day at the Democracy Wall at 10am. From there we will march to Tiananmen Square!

At the mention of the word 'demonstration', the mood of the meeting turned sombre. It suddenly dawned on us that, if we made the threat, we must be prepared to carry it out whatever the consequences. A heavy silence shrouded the dark room, as each of us sunk into our own private thoughts. Slowly, one by one, the founders of the Stars began to speak.

I can't remember who said it, possibly A Cheng. 'Surely we shall get a reply; the Mayor won't want a disturbance on National Day?'

But I remember thinking, 'Will he really answer a bunch of students and amateur artists?'

Huang Rui was not at all happy with the proposal and looking at Liu Qing said, 'We are artists, not political activists. '

It was the other political activist, Xu Wenli who replied,

'Your right as artists to exhibit your work has been attacked. You can't avoid it. You have no choice but to fight for your rights.'

Liu Qing argued passionately, 'This is a momentous day. You have a unique opportunity to achieve a victory for the Democracy Movement.' He repeated: 'The Stars Art Show was popular and was legal. It was the police action that was illegal. That means we can march upholding the law. But you Stars have to make the decision. Only you five leaders can decide.'

Wang Keping stood up, 'We made this problem. We made the threat. If we compromise now, we are dead. We're riding the tiger. The bigger the problem we make, the safer we will be. Think of the Guomintang (Sara – The Civil War). Nothing happened to the people at the top but the little people were killed.'

Ma Desheng enthused, 'Let's do the fucking march' but Huang Rui shook his head repeating, 'We're artists – not politicians.'

The stars in the sky were shrouded in grey cloud and, looking at my watch through the grey cloud of smoke in the room, I knew Weiwei would be worried. Exhausted with emotion, I reluctantly made my way home but I didn't sleep much that night. In the morning, my friends filled me in.

When the discussion started to repeat itself, Xu Wenli said it was time to vote so Liu Qing asked each of the founding Stars in turn whether they were in favour of marching. Wang immediately supported Ma Desheng.

Lui Qing turned to Qu Leilei who had yet to comment.

'I agree. Let's march.' said Leilei.

Liu Qing and Xu Wenli punched the air with their fists. Three to one in favour of marching!

Huang Rui, who had been the most active in organising the show, had lost but he said, 'I don't agree with marching but I'll still support you.'

They dispatched the final notice as the clock struck midnight on the thirtieth and waited for a response and waited ...

Looking back, Sara, we were naïve. Most of the twenty who had pictures at the show thought the authorities would reply. Many of them thought the answer would be 'No' but we were unprepared for the deathly silence.

Lui Qing and Xu Wenli probably suspected this would happen. Everyone gathered together on the evening of October 30th prepared to wait patiently, but the tension mounted by the minute as we watched the clock. When the midnight hour struck, still there was no response to our ultimatum. We looked at each other to test our resolve as the realisation that we would not get a reply loomed over us. I don't think any of us got much sleep before dawn and October 1st. Anxious about me going on the protest march, Weiwei insisted on coming along, saying, 'If you are arrested then I'll be arrested with you.'

Lui Qing and Xu Wenli had put up posters so we expected their supporters would join us.

8.00 am October 1st 1979: The Stars march to Tiananmen.

An autumn chill was in the air as the fallen leaves danced around in the wind. The weather seemed to echo our restlessness. Huang Rui, Ma Desheng, Wang Keping and Qu Leilei stood at the front. After the two politicians, Liu Qing and Xu Wenli had made speeches, Huang Rui stood up and described the show and why we were there. More and more people had gathered to hear them. Ten o'clock, zero hour, approached and still no reply from the government! If we were to march we must leave soon.

Ma Desheng gave an emotional speech on behalf of the Stars. He laid his hand on his chest and then made a sweeping gesture towards the crowd.

'Do you know what today is? This is our National Day. Our nation is like our mother. She has suffered so much and even though she is worn, she is still beautiful. We are her children. We produce art from our hearts for our mother. We cry for the pain she has suffered and want to rebuild her beauty. We want to express our feelings through love of art. The Beijing Government was given notice and every opportunity to reply. We explained that our exhibition was our contribution to National Day and yet the police stopped it.

They trampled our rights as artists. We will march for justice.'

With that he unfurled the banner: 'In politics we want democracy and in art we want freedom.'

Wang Keping and Qu Leilei held it up over him. We all cheered as Ma on his crutches led the way. Word had got around and more than two thousand people joined us as we marched towards the Central Government buildings. I drew strength from a vision of the light of stars penetrating darkness. I felt strong until I saw the wall of dazzling white. Lined up in front of us were three rows of white uniformed police, hundreds of them, blocking the road ahead. You could touch the tension; it was so intense we froze into an eerie silence.

Then someone burst into song, *The Internationale*, and the sound inspired us. We all joined in and it helped overcome our fear. But Weiwei grabbed my hand and said, 'Let's go.'

I didn't want to leave and struggled, but then let him take me to the side. The singing stopped as suddenly as it had begun and the front row looked over their shoulders. Most of the marchers were melting away into the sides of the street and I was with a group that hesitated thirty yards away, leaving just twenty of them facing the massive police cordon. I felt like a coward as the police told us, 'Our orders are to stop you going on to Tiananmen.'

They were expecting resistance but Liu Qing and Xu Wenli said, 'Let's follow police instructions and change our route.'

Amazingly, confrontation was avoided. Relieved, I followed the twenty as they turned right and headed in the direction of the Beijing local government building. The crowd reformed and we all watched admiringly as Wang Keping and Qu Leilei climbed its steps and held the banner high. Huang Rui made a speech and Liu Qing and Xu Wenli went inside. They found just three people inside this huge building – everyone else was on holiday. Of course those three couldn't make a decision – there is a rigid hierarchy in the Chinese bureaucracy.

As if someone had uttered some magic words, the foreign press arrived with cameras flashing and four Stars were filmed as they stood on the steps. When the three came out of the building, Lui Qing waved his hand.

'We have delivered our message. We dismiss the march.'

Weiwei turned to me, 'Liu Qing and Wenli are shrewd. Come on. Hurry, we are going home.'

Weiwei was right. The police were regrouping and preparing to surround us and given another twenty minutes, we would all have been arrested. The timing was perfect. Tired but excited, we made our way home. And the day's events were reported in the world press so our protest couldn't simply be ignored. My father told me that the Mayor was personally supportive, although I'm not sure how he knew this.

And six weeks later, we triumphed when a jubilant Huang Rui told us, 'We have won! We can mount a show inside a gallery!'

Freedom of expression, freedom of speech and thought and deed had triumphed. It felt like the dawn of a new China. On the evening I received the news, I looked up at the sky. The stars in the heavens seemed to shine brighter than usual.

Although Jiang Feng, the Chairman of the Artists Association agreed that we could exhibit, his opinion hadn't changed. He said, 'When these people (The Stars) realise that the mass of the people don't understand their work, they will learn and change their ways.'

Triumph and misery

I just wished I had more time to paint. Between work at the publishing house, studying English, the domestic chores and Weiwei, when could I pick up a brush?

Weiwei was learning to share the cooking but just like here, Sara, men ignored the housework. If my mother had been alive we would have shared the chores.

It was frustrating but I was determined not to be left out. Short of time, I worked on a revised version of *Unknown Builders of the Great Wall.* When the show opened, on November 23rd, my thoughts were distracted because I had missed my monthly period.

The gallery was just inside the exquisite Beihai Park at a time of year when almost the only visitors were the skaters. A big grin spread across the park keeper's gaunt face. 'I haven't ever seen so many people here in the winter before.'

For a tiny fee of two cents, his job was to look after bicycles and he was doing a roaring trade. The Chairman was proved wrong because the people may not have understood the art exactly but they were thrilled by the new experience.

Standing in front of my picture, I began to believe that I could become a true artist. My hand strayed to my belly. Was it possible that I, Little Winter, could create life and art, my own art and my own child, neither dictated by decree but instead born of love? This was such a radical concept when both had so long been suppressed. What had I done to deserve such good fortune? I wished my mother could see me now painting with The Stars. This was what she fought and struggled for.

I'll always see in my mind's eye two striking images from the Beihai show. Red, White and Black was by Li Shuang, the most impressive female artist in the show. She said, 'Red represents blood, white represents terror and black is a metaphor of the gloomy situation'.

That was how I discovered that I was not the only person deeply affected by Jiang He's poem about Zhang Zhixin. The difference was that Li Shuang had painted her reaction to it. The tortured figure was in black and red. The red line at her neck was surely the moment when Zhang's throat was cut to prevent her from shouting. In the same mood was her violent woodblock print titled *Struggle*. Before my eyes I saw and felt imprisonment. The isolation was dreadful – the vertical bars, diagonal shadows and the lone figure seated on the floor.

The show was a triumph and this comment by one visitor was typical of the reaction: 'Oh, The Stars! Your painting is not painted for entertainment or leisure. You are crying and shouting! To get rid of life's sufferings, may you forever march at the front.'

Many of The Stars artists were painting the horror that people had witnessed but we didn't feel sad. We were changing China. The horror was to be the past not the future. Some of us celebrated with wine, tobacco and music. Weiwei just shared my joy and didn't show a wrinkle of envy. He had taught me to smoke but I had only rarely drunk alcohol and then only a single glass. Having a few glasses meant it went straight to my head. As I climbed the stairs to our apartment, I waved my arms and sang, 'We are the stars'. On the steps our neighbour's cabbages appeared in my tipsy vision like silvery moons. I picked one up and half fell down the stairs as I threw it through the door into the night sky. Weiwei came to my rescue. He guided me to our room saying, 'Forget the man in the moon, come back down to earth and to me Snowdrop. You need earth to thrive not moonshine.'

He tucked me in bed and went into the street to sweep up the bits of cabbage and replaced my neighbour's vegetable with one of ours.

The trial of Wei Jingsheng

Sara, so now you know that I am who I am because of The Stars Art Movement. I hope you have understood from my description that even though some Stars didn't like it, we were part of a scene that included the underground magazines that were full of political ideas. It was as if we were all ingredients in one big stew. That pot toppled over and one of the reasons was the trial of a friend of Weiwei's. His name was Wei Jingsheng.

I should have known that my delight and self-confidence would be short-lived. Our lives would be tossed in the air by unseen jugglers and I had no idea where we would land. It was all down to chance that Weiwei was at the High Court on October 15th, the date set for his friend Wei Jingsheng's trial. Jingsheng had introduced us to Today, which led to my involvement with The Stars, so I felt especially grateful to him.

He was arrested on March 29th 1979 after publishing an article on the Democracy Wall calling for a genuine general election and warning people to make sure that, 'Deng Xiaoping (our new head of state) does not degenerate into a dictator.'

The top media, *The People's Daily* and the *New China News Agency*, were to be present at his trial on charges of treason. Weiwei was sent to take pictures.

Usually autumn in Beijing is golden, but as Weiwei left home that day the clouded sky felt low and oppressive. The theatre-like court near to Tiananmen Square seats one thousand people on two floors and it was full. The audience was mostly magistrates and top police officers from all over China come to learn how to manage political trials for this was to be a show trial. During the Cultural Revolution, there had been lots of trials of opponents of the Gang of Four but those kangaroo courts were meant to have become a thing of the past. I believed that what happened to Zhang Zhixin could never happen again. At least Jingsheng was to be allowed to speak.

When he came home, I pressed Weiwei to describe every detail. He sat at that worn old table which had witnessed so many life lessons taught me by my parents. He sighed and put his head in his hands. I waited. He looked at his camera on the table and it seemed to inspire a picture in his mind. He began to speak in slow measured tones.

'Jingsheng was brought in flanked by two officers and one followed behind.'

Weiwei handed me a photograph. I looked at Wei Jingsheng facing his accusers and cried. They had tried to strip him of his dignity by shaving his head and dressing him in shapeless prison clothes. Weiwei squeezed my hands and looked me directly in the eyes.

'Snowdrop – despite his prison clothes and his shaved head – he looked defiant.'

I squeezed his hand in return, sniffed, and asked him to please tell me everything.

'We were told that the defendant would defend himself. Then they asked his name and read out the list of charges, the main ones were betraying state secrets and counter-revolution.'

Sara, I had only met him as part of a crowd. Only when I arrived in California did I learn the origins of his passion for democracy. I don't think any American can really visualise the scene he describes. Do you remember how Jia and I headed west on our revolutionary travelling? Well, so did Wei Jingsheng in 1966. The train he was travelling on paused at a station so small that it didn't even have a platform. That chance stop set him on a career that led to this court room. This is how he described it in his book.

> *'People were begging for food, waving desperate hands at the window. The passenger beside me said, 'If they are not landlord elements then they must be idlers. Let them starve.'*
> *But I was sixteen years old and felt sorry for a woman in rags beneath my window and leaned out to give her some cakes. I twisted my head back and left my hand hanging in mid-air. For what I had just seen was quite beyond my imagination and up till then unbelievable. The woman with her hair over her shoulders was a girl of about seventeen or eighteen. From a distance, the ashes and mud smeared over her looked like clothing.*
> *'There's a lot like this around,' the passenger confided with a knowing chuckle. 'Some are quite pretty, and if you give them some food then without it costing anything you can ...'*
> *But I was shocked into forming a question in my mind. I believed that socialism was meant to banish poverty. I asked myself, 'How can such things happen?''*

Sara you won't understand this but questions can be dangerous and that question led to his first wall poster, Democracy: the Fifth Modernisation, *and to this trial, fighting for his life.*

My charismatic husband was a wonderful mimic and at this point he assumed Judge Zhang Fengee's clipped accent. In different circumstances, it would have made me laugh.

'The accused, Wei Jingsheng, 29 years old, is employed as a labourer by the Peking Municipal Parks Department. On 29th March 1979, the accused was arrested for counter-revolutionary crimes by the Peking Public Security Bureau. The case was solved and referred to this court for investigation and indictment. The investigation has verified that the accused, Wei Jingsheng, has committed the following crimes: 1) passing Chinese military secrets to foreigners; and 2) disseminating counter-revolutionary propaganda and inciting counter-revolutionary activities.'

Weiwei said the prosecution spent a long time cross-examining him on things he had written in Exploration.

'You slandered our socialist system as "a feudal monarchy concealing itself under a cloak of socialism". Why did you write that? What did you mean by this?'

Point by point, our friend refuted the charges against him but it made no difference. Weiwei said, 'It was like watching a play which I knew had a tragic ending. They wanted him out of the way but needed an excuse. The excuse? He had talked to foreign correspondents. They accused him of accepting foreign money. He replied that the only money he made was from selling magazines.'

Weiwei sounded almost awed as he described what happened next.

'He looked bright and calm but his mind was dagger-sharp. His reply sounded confident as he faced the audience and said, "In the eyes of the public prosecutor, my discussions with English and French foreign correspondents are seen as treasonable acts. Yet when Party Chairman, Hua Guofeng, met with the same journalists from Western European nations, he quite clearly addressed each of them as 'my friends'."

The prosecutor quoted Wei Jingsheng's opinion of the need for general elections to validate office and said "You mean our great leader is illegal?"

Our friend wasn't fazed by the sudden intake of breath in the audience and answered, "In theory that is true." Then Judge Zhang shouted at him calling him "a poisonous viper"!'

'Did he really say that?' I asked.

'Yes and more. But I can't remember his entire harangue... it went on for so long. Wei Jingsheng was amazing. Throughout the trial he stayed calm.

Zhang wanted to debate the minutiae to trip him up but he was ready for him. "I put all my thoughts in my writing: if you are interested we can discuss them, at a different time and in a different place."

Snowdrop, he knew he was only present for one reason: to be sentenced. They called witnesses.'

Weiwei shook his head as the shock spread over my face as he described one of them. Yang was Wei Jingsheng's closest friend and joint editor of *Exploration*. Weiwei said, 'Yes, Yang's face burnt crimson as I trained my camera on him. He confirmed the meetings with foreigners – he would know, wouldn't he? After all, he was there at the time! And he hardly ever raised his head, Snowdrop. I didn't get one single shot of him full face.'

It took little imagination on our part to understand the pressure and the threats he was under to betray his best friend. But betrayal is betrayal.

Weiwei lit another cigarette before he continued. 'The Prosecutor asked him, "Do you know this man?" Question after question, Wei Jingsheng's response was unwavering. Whatever happened, he put the blame on himself.

"Yes, I asked him to do it".

"Yes, that was my responsibility."

"Yes, I told him to do it." He stood there, in that crowded room saying those words, protecting his traitorous friend, so completely alone.

Snowdrop, I knew this was a kangaroo trial but I couldn't help it. My camera shook when I heard that word "guilty" of betraying secrets and of counter-revolution. But he stayed so incredibly calm and made such an impressive speech before they passed sentence – he is such a brave man. If only I had his courage ...'

As I put out a hand to touch him, Weiwei took out another cigarette.

'You are brave – you were incredibly brave to put up those posters against the Gang of Four but please, take my father's advice. Think carefully before you do anything. Now tell me what he said. No, first, tell me, what was the sentence?'

'The prosecution called for a "severe sentence". They said it was because he had refused to plead guilty.'

I shivered. The death penalty for those found guilty of treason was common.

'He got fifteen years.'

Chinese jails are dreadful places, beyond dreadful. Weiwei didn't look at me but paced around the room. He knew: he had been there. Then he grabbed my hand and said, 'Come on – let's go to the Democracy Wall.'

Liu Qing had pasted Wei Jingsheng's defence on the Democracy Wall. Everything Weiwei had told me was written there in black and white. We learned through the grapevine that someone in court that day had secretly recorded it.

'That must have taken a lot of courage, Snowdrop. Who could have done it? They may suspect me.'

It wasn't Weiwei. It was the Stars artist, Qu Leilei. He worked for China TV as a lighting technician and had recorded it using a tiny tape recorder. Since Wei's defence became common knowledge in Beijing, we believed that Leilei had saved Wei Jingsheng's life. He would not be forgotten.

I wondered where he could have got such a tiny tape recorder. The source turned out to be the French embassy. The best known female Star, Li Shuang had fallen in love with a French diplomat. We enjoyed teasing her boyfriend and gave him a Chinese name, Bai Tian Xiang (Lucky Day). The political elite soon realised that Bai was the source of the recorder. They hated him but his diplomatic immunity made it difficult to get rid of him so, instead, they targeted Li Shuang, poor thing.

Li Shuang was only released from the labour camp when French ministers argued her case with Deng Xiaoping. I didn't get to see her again, not even to say goodbye, because they wanted her out of the country. Her arrival in Paris and her marriage to Bai Tian Xiang was huge news in Europe. Photographs of her were all over the French papers. She made The Stars famous in France. I longed to visit Paris and see all the great paintings in the Louvre.

Sara, you probably won't understand it now but when you are older, you will see what a fine mind Wei Jingsheng had. These are his words pasted on the Democracy Wall: 'Those who forbid the critical treatment of Marxism are engaged in the process of transforming Marxism into a religious faith.'

Sara, that means that any kind of fanatical dogma, religious or secular, is to be feared by rational people. You will probably find this story hard to understand. Sometimes you think I am too serious and should lighten up. I do try but I don't want to forget brave people who try to change the world for the better. You can imagine my feelings of admiration and sadness as I stood in front of the Democracy Wall, knowing that, because of those words which to you, Sara, probably sound very boring, Wei Jingsheng would spend fifteen years in jail!

Because his defence was on the Democracy Wall for all to read, protests against the trial and sentence were heard around the world. Amnesty International would not allow him to be forgotten, but at the time I knew none of that.

The wall comes tumbling down

We weren't there when the police tore down Liu Qing's pamphlets in support of Wei Jingsheng. A student activist friend of Liu promptly replaced them and was just as promptly arrested. When brave Liu headed straight for the police station asking, 'What grounds do you have for seizing him?' they replied, 'reactionary handbills.'

Liu responded, 'They are transcripts of the trial of Wei Jingsheng. The People's Daily have talked about it to the whole world. What is there illegal about pasting transcripts?' We thought that maybe since the world was now watching the phenomenon of the Stars Art Movement, we might be protected a little. We were wrong.

Wei Jinsheng's trial may have been public and gone global, but that did not stop them from arresting Liu Qing that night. Weiwei and I had a quiet discussion with my father as we sat together around our talking table. He looked sad as he talked about the trials.

'You know Wei Jingsheng's mistake? If he had kept his *dàzìbào* theoretical, he would probably have escaped trial. His mistake was mentioning Deng Xiaoping by name. It will take a generation at least for that to change in China. We have had an Emperor for two thousand years. Deng is doing some good things but he won't allow anyone to threaten his position.'

Father looked stern and said, 'I don't want to visit you two in prison, so be careful what you say. No one can stop you thinking but they can stop you talking.'

That frustrated and despairing mask fixed itself once again to Weiwei's face. When he was happy, Weiwei was handsome and animated but when his features became wooden and fossilised, he appeared dull and plain.

Sara, I hope these two stories of the Stars Art Movement and Wei Jingsheng's trial, of our lack of freedom of thought and speech, will help you understand why my struggle to think for myself was not easy. To you, politics is boring because you have freedom to say what you like and don't understand what it is to be afraid, what it is like to have almost no control over your destiny.

The one hundred metre long Democracy Wall came tumbling down never to be rebuilt and its dust smothered our dreams of a new China. I was sad thinking of those three bright young men languishing in jail; they seemed like friends, even though they had not spoken to me. While we celebrated together the success of The Stars' official exhibition, in the glorious Beihai Park, they were locked up in solitary confinement. But I had other things to occupy my mind. It was obvious that I was pregnant. I was sad and angry about Liu, I was celebrating The Stars and secretly cherishing the fruit of the love Weiwei and I shared. I was overwhelmed by a confusion of emotion; I didn't know how to handle it or when to tell Weiwei. And my father: I knew he would love a grandchild. But I didn't get the chance.

At work, I felt a sudden dreadful pain. My colleagues were worried and took me to hospital where I miscarried. They were short-staffed and brisk. There is no shortage of people in China so sympathy was not supplied. As I took the bus home, I looked out of tearful eyes at the streams of bicycles. I was empty, hollow inside. But I didn't say anything to Weiwei and my father. They hadn't known I was pregnant so I thought to save them the sorrow.

The next evening, Weiwei met one of my colleagues in the street. She meant well. The trip to the hospital was mentioned. So when he got home his anger that I hadn't told him I was pregnant, that I hadn't told him about the miscarriage, all came rushing out. We started shouting at each other louder and louder until Ba knocked on his study/bedroom wall.

We stopped and looked at each other and involuntary tears welled up and not just mine, Weiwei's too.

'Xiaodong, you must promise me. From now on there must be no secrets between us. It's hard enough for me having to button my lips and suppress my ideas and live in small shoes only able to dance to the tune of my superiors. If our life together is bound by things not spoken, I don't think I could bear it.'

I had lost our baby, I didn't want to lose Weiwei's heart too: I promised. When Weiwei saw I was sincere and sorry, he held me close and forgave me. There was no way Ba could not have heard our 'conversation' but as a conservative Chinese man, he said nothing. He looked sad; he really looked forward to becoming a YeYe (grandfather).

For months, I was not really living, just having the vital life signs to show I existed. Spring was in the air before I saw any of the Stars again and then I bumped into Huang Rui.

'Little Winter, amazing news. You won't believe it.'

'Try and make me,' I said, pleased to see him.

'You had better get busy with your art if you want a picture hung inside the National Gallery!'

'You boys love teasing me.'

'Yes I do, but this time I am being serious. We can have a show inside. Yes seriously, inside – not on the railings! It opens on August 24th.'

Weiwei was so enthusiastic, he fizzed.

'What shall I do? Am I good enough?' I asked him.

'Of course you're good enough.'

'Some of the others are pushing the boundaries and want freedom. I suppose I do too but, more than that, I think I want beauty. I would like to paint the Great Wall but in colour, each brick a different hue, each brick representing a human being, each one unique. What do you think? Weiwei, I don't want you to get into trouble. You have already had enough problems to deal with.'

'Snowdrop, that is wonderful. It is so poetic. I have an idea. I might feel more content if I try to write poetry. You are showing what I feel. If I say it in poems and not dàzìbàos, I may feel more liberated but not end up incarcerated like Wei Jingsheng.'

'Please, Hero, please paint your poem on my picture. It's something we can do together.'

And that is how Weiwei began to free his spirit. He discovered that the earth, the wind, the moon and our ancient folk stories gave him inspiration. On the painted clay bricks in my picture, he wrote about the goddess Nuwa, who created man and woman out of clay. Just the right words for each human brick. Imagine our excitement when we went to see our picture in the National Gallery!

The Stars become famous

Sara, there had never been a more exciting show in China. A quarter of a million people came to see it. Can you imagine so many people queuing for an art exhibition?

It was a landmark in the history of contemporary Chinese art. Reporters from all around the world came and wrote about it. They saw it as a glimmer of change in China. I don't think anyone mentioned our picture, it wasn't as ground-breaking as the other Stars' work, but the response to the show helped me to emerge from under my cloud of despair.

I just couldn't believe my eyes when I arrived on 24th and saw the queues of people being marshalled by police! They actually joked with us, because they were making sure the huge crowds waited in an orderly manner! Weiwei came to see it. He rushed from one room to another and then began at the beginning again. We were all caught up in the excitement of the discussion that followed.

The show was called Xing Xing Huazhan. Because it took place in the National Gallery with full official approval, it was reviewed by newspapers and journals all over the world. John Gittings, writing for *The Guardian*, a British newspaper, was typical of the international response welcoming the dawn of an official tolerance of experimental art.

'Some of the most successful works are found among the woodcuts and other graphics. A powerful set of eight black-and-white sketches by Qu Leilei on *The Motherland* shows the Chinese people oppressed – in the final scene flat on the ground – but still asserting their nationhood. Woodcuts by Ma DeSheng show the patient weary faces of a peasant with his ox ...'

He didn't mention Wang Keping's ironic wooden sculpture of Mao as Buddha nor Weiwei and my *A Million Bricks*. No one could fail to notice that our art had broken free of the way Mao had been deified. We were all practising self-expression or *ziwobiaoxian*. We were not aware but the political content alarmed the authorities. They were happy when we criticised the Gang of Four but not prepared to accept criticism of Mao.

Our success led to feverish debate. There was a magazine called *Art Monthly*. I could hardly believe my eyes when Qu Leilei gave me a copy which included his article *Art for the sake of self-expression* (*ziwobiaoxian de yishu*). It prompted a debate that continued for two years.

Weiwei began what he had always wanted: to write. He entered the intellectual debate and challenged the supremacy of ideology. He wrote that we needed human values as well as theoretical ones. Spies were everywhere and it was only a matter of time before he was summoned to the Beijing Security Bureau. They have a long memory. His spell in prison was on record as was his friendship with Wei Jingsheng. But this was meant as a warning shot so they let him go.

That night he looked so gloomy.

'Snowdrop, they will always keep me in small shoes.'

Sara, I love seeing you running. We take for granted that we can move freely. Before the revolution in China, the binding of women's feet, if you were not a peasant, was common. That is why the phrase 'keeping someone in small shoes' has so much significance in China. I have been lucky in the men whom I have loved and who have loved me: my father, Weiwei and your father. They all wanted me to express myself and develop what little talent I have. Their only concern was for my safety. That is why I struggle to understand the strength of patriarchal societies, restricting women with bound feet or behind the veil or by unequal laws. I wish so much that you will have my good fortune in knowing good men. My fear for you is that you may meet one of those men who will want total control over you.

Foot binding was one of the means of keeping women under control. That was what Weiwei meant; his life was constrained, like being able only to walk short distances in pain on bound feet. He despaired of ever being able to live the kind of life he wanted and develop his skills. I believe, with hindsight, that he was depressed but we didn't use those kinds of words then. Living here in the US for so long, I too think like that now. I see everyone as individuals, their moods affected by their experiences but my eyes were not open then to understanding that. I was worried about Weiwei, his passion even for making love seemed to have waned. I wanted to talk to his sister, Jia, but instead found myself talking to a friend I worked with whom I thought I could trust.

She said, 'Have you heard of Freud?'

I shook my head.

'I'll try and get you a book about him.'

Sara, I read it with such mixed feelings. In the end I showed it to Weiwei.

He looked really thoughtful but not convinced.

'It doesn't look that scientific to me. His conclusions are based on just a few rich patients – that's hardly a credible sample, is it?' As he blew sceptical smoke rings, I blew rings too and mine mingled with his in hope.

Berkeley, October 2010

Sara, I felt like tearing up all that I have written so far and your father stopped me throwing this manuscript on the fire. You have refused to go to your Saturday Mandarin classes. I asked myself, 'Why bother writing this now?' Not only will you not want to read any of this but you won't be able to read it for yourself if you don't learn Chinese. Your life is gilded with privilege, and yet you rebel against authority.

At your age I was already revolutionary, travelling far from my parents, mature and responsible. In my story, I have arrived at a good time in my life and was enjoying remembering The Stars. So I'll write on for a while at least and then decide whether to continue.

Beijing 1981: The Stars continue to shine

The success of The Stars' Shows and the encouragement of Li Xianting gave me hope that I could pursue a career in art. So I decided to sit the exams for admittance to the National Academy of Art and follow my true ambition. I dreamed of putting my amateur days behind me and becoming a professional artist. I wanted to study for a Master's.

I applied and felt so happy when I received the certificate that enabled me to enter the competition for places. It took a whole week because we had to sit nine exams including art theory, Classical Chinese, politics, sketching, drawing, colour painting and painting to a theme. Each took half a day. I was nervous because all the other students were quite well known already.

The system of exams in China has for over a thousand years been anonymous to prevent nepotism. Only one person has the list of names that correspond to the numbers given to the entrants. The invigilators mark the papers not knowing the identity of the applicant. Each subject was marked by specialists in the field. When I heard that I had won a place, I was so happy that we had a party with our friends to celebrate.

At the party, Chang asked, 'Did you hear about Qu Leilei?'

'I think he got through too, didn't he?'

'Well he came fourth in the exam but they haven't given him a place. The Security Bureau must have vetoed it. I think you have his place, Xiaodong.'

After that I didn't feel like celebrating. We soon left the restaurant and cycled home. As soon as we got through the door, I cried my heart out and nothing Weiwei could say could console me.

'I ought to say no. I ought to tell them they have picked the wrong person.'

Weiwei said. 'Let's discuss this in the morning. We'll go for a walk in the park like we always do when times are tough.' We headed for Beihai Park, which held good memories. As we sat in the shade, he talked me round.

'How will it help Leilei, you not taking up the place? They won't let him have the place because he recorded Wei Jingsheng's defence, you know that. This is your chance and you will regret it for the rest of your life if you don't go.'

My next painting was part collage and I called it *Shoes*. I knew Weiwei and Leilei would understand the meaning of those very tiny shoes.

The Stars were glamorous so I hoped for a brighter future even though I wasn't one of its founders. The world media coverage meant lots of foreigners wanted to meet us. I'll never forget going to the American Embassy. For the first time in our lives we heard western pop music and some of the staff tried to teach us disco dancing. Because it was banned in China, except in the foreign quarter, it was forbidden fruit. Of course, we were watched and the following day Weiwei was once again hauled in by the Security Bureau. The Stars were feted but for Weiwei to go within yards of a foreign journalist outside his work was dangerous. It wasn't worth it. After that, we shunned the limelight and hid in the shadows.

Our time of free expression didn't last. After Wei Jingsheng's trial, none of us really expected it to. The editor of *Fine Art Magazine*, Li Xianting, who had championed The Stars within the academy and organised our official exhibition was in trouble. There was a backlash, following the commission to paint a mural for the new Beijing International Airport. The chosen artist, He Yuan Yungsheng called it *Water Splashing Festival*. Seeing his work in progress, we felt optimistic that here was new art that was going to be public art. But when it was unveiled, the condemnation was vile. The reason: Yuan's design included nude female figures. The odd thing about the Cultural Revolution, with its emphasis on the rebellion of youth, was that sex was taboo. I was only just becoming aware of the sexual revolution that had taken place at that time in the West. Conservative elements campaigned against our openness to this 'pollution'. Because of them, this beautiful airport mural was boarded up in 1981. Person by person, artwork by artwork, we were being forced back into our small shoes.

The Stars speak out

I was a student when Li Xianting, whom we starting calling The Godfather of Chinese Contemporary Art, organised a conference at the Central Academy inviting the five founders of the Stars to participate; despite the opposition, fresh ideas were still bubbling to the surface. Speaking to a room packed and overflowing into the corridor, Wang Keping, Huang Rui, Ma DeSheng, A Cheng and Qu Leilei each in turn gave their opinion as the audience outside strained to hear. Most voiced the opinion that art in

China had gone wrong because there was no interest in anything except propaganda, but A Cheng argued that art should still represent the people and not the individual. This type of discussion was unusual; opinions differed but each was given respect. That didn't find favour with the conservative political elite! Power swung like a pendulum as, flexing their muscles, they introduced 'The Anti-Spiritual Pollution Campaign'. Spiritual Pollution meant ideas of bourgeois liberalism or western ideas of the freedom of the individual. Deng Xiaoping endorsed the Anti-Spiritual Pollution campaign in October 1983. A pragmatist on the economic reform he may have been, but he drew the line at humanism.

'People working in the ideological field,' he said, 'must not spread spiritual pollution ... they have engaged in discussions of the value of the human being, humanism and alienation and have only been interested in criticising socialism, not capitalism.'

Jealous old cadres were obsessed by the trivia of daily life and they tried to turn the clock back towards the Cultural Revolution; they wanted to clone us in the same style of clothing and the same hairstyle. But I witnessed lots of little rebellions. Turning the corner on my bicycle one day, I rode headlong into a group of girls buying lipstick from a market stall. I apologised but they just giggled and one of them grinned at me saying, 'Were you trying to stop me buying a tube of spiritual pollution?' Good joke, no?

That's how different life was with Mao and the Gang of Four gone. Now, the reaction was to joke about it. People weren't afraid and humour made the conservatives look ridiculous. It worked much better than street protest. In the meantime, however, The Stars were influenced by western ideas of free expression in art and so were regarded as pollutants of the worst kind. Our third exhibition planned for the National Gallery was cancelled, and the campaign brought down Li Xianting for his support of The Stars. His worst crime was printing articles on abstract art.

One day my fellow Stars artist, Wang Keping, visited us. From his grin, we guessed he had good news. He was marrying a French woman and said, 'We are going to live in France. You must come to our wedding party. Promise? Don't let us down. Be there.'

The party was in the spacious accommodation enjoyed by wealthy westerners and I admit to rare pangs of jealousy. I loved my father but Weiwei and I dreamed of a place of our own. Then Huang Rui married a Japanese woman and left for Tokyo and Ai Weiwei for America. The Stars were going out!

'Do you think we should try to leave, Weiwei? Wouldn't it be wonderful to live in an apartment like that one.'

'I don't think they would give me a passport; you might be luckier, Snowdrop.'

'Are you suggesting we part?' I asked. I must have looked ready to burst into tears.

'No, of course not, but I don't want to hold you back. You'll soon have your MA and I bet you could get a scholarship to an American university. I've heard that they like to attract gifted students from all over the world at the PhD level.'

'How can I leave you?' I said. 'I don't want our baby to grow up without a father.'

'Snowdrop ... are you ... really ... is it possible ... Come here.' Before long we shared the news with my father who wanted to buy up the entire contents of the wine shop!

Hard times

Sara, at that time, the only posts involved in art and design were government controlled. Deng's economic reforms were starting in the south, in the new city of Shenzhen, but in Beijing things were much the same.

Things had improved a little for Weiwei. Because he was good at what he did, he began to work on films and they were becoming more creative. Even China TV, freed from the Gang of Four's iron grip, was producing shows people actually enjoyed and related to.

We watched a Chinese film called *Hard Times*, the most popular film in 1982. It was about students sent to the countryside, just as Weiwei and I had been to Manchuria. Weiwei told me, 'The true story took place in a hilly area where it is always raining and so they had to find somewhere more suitable for filming. That's why it is in Yunnan; the weather is better but the landscape's similar.'

I fell in love with the ancient village where water buffalos waded through idyllic streams. It looked so romantic that I persuaded Weiwei to take me there in the summer of eighty-four and I am sure that was where our son was conceived. Weiwei was being used on similar films that tackled the misery of the years of the Cultural Revolution. Because Deng Xiaoping had suffered so much at that time, a new openness about those years was approved. Weiwei felt more liberated working on these kinds of films based on books known as skull literature. His small shoes had expanded by two sizes! There were now holes in the toes! Star artist A Cheng wrote some novels set during the Cultural Revolution. *Hai zi wang* (King of Children) would be made into a successful film.

Skull literature tried to go beyond the superficial and delve inside people's minds and emotions and connect to nature and old Daoist instincts.

The directors were flexible so it was easier for him to take some time off. I remember sketching on the hillside and thinking how beautiful China was and feeling optimistic. In *Hard Times*, the village was called Lost Times Village and the village where they filmed changed its name to that. The film had made it a popular destination and it was prospering because of tourists like us.

Weiwei worked for a while with a director called Huang Jian Zhong who asked after me because he had been to The Stars' show and remembered my *Great Wall* picture. Weiwei explained that I would soon have my MA from the Academy. Huang suggested I come and see him. Weiwei took me to meet him in the courtyard house within the studio compound, where he lived. I noticed how well the two got on. They were both outgoing but their accents were in real contrast. Huang Jian Zhong was from Quanzhou, so had a marked southern accent.

When I said, 'I loved *Little Blossom* ...' he beamed with pleasure. I hadn't meant it as flattery but it did me no harm. That film, set during the Civil War, wasn't the usual story of a soldier's heroism inspired by communist rhetoric. It was a real breakthrough because it focused on his relationship with his two sisters, one natural and the other adopted but both called Blossom. The humanity in this film stood out like flowers blooming in the desert. We ended up watching one of his favourite films of all time, Citizen Kane. Before we left, he told me to see him once I had my MA and he would see if I could work on set designs. But my pregnancy was complicating things so the director suggested I join him once our baby was settled in nursery.

It was unusual in China for the father to be present at the birth, but Weiwei wanted to see his baby born and I wanted him there. My father did some arm-twisting. He was much in demand in those days, flying all over the country inspecting engineering projects. Somehow he managed to get me a private room. There was little privacy in Chinese hospitals even on labour wards. We persuaded the hospital that since I was an only child and my mother was dead, they should let Weiwei be with me. Thanks to that private room, he was there to see his son born. He looked so nervous and ill at ease. Worrying about him took my mind off the labour, which felt endless, but then, in a flash, our son swam out. Weiwei had the first glimpse of him and that watery memory will always be with me. I can close my eyes and see them both. We named him Wang meaning hope.

Ba was so proud of him. He held him in such a tender loving embrace that I wanted to cry. I wondered if he had held me like that.

'No, of course not, I didn't like your hair and threw you in the dust-bin.' I knew Ba loved me and was proud of me but he didn't often say it. Somehow with Wang, though, his face was more expressive and his love shone through.

Father arranged for a nanny when Wang was six months so that I could begin work at the studios. Once he was two, he started at nursery. Then Ba moved out leaving us to have the flat to ourselves. He moved into a new flat near the Agricultural Exhibition Hall in Nongzhangguan, but he made sure that he saw Wang every week.

Life felt so much better and our optimism grew because, although Deng Xiaoping really called the shots, the General Secretary of the Communist party's influence grew. It was thanks to Hu Yaobang that father was influential again. Hu tried to rehabilitate the people who were persecuted during the Cultural Revolution. He was a pragmatist and was changing so many things for the better and Deng was liberalising the economy. Hu even ordered the withdrawal of thousands of Chinese Han soldiers from the Tibet Autonomous Region believing that Tibetans should be allowed to administer their own affairs. He insisted that Han Chinese who remained should learn Tibetan and wanted, in his words, 'to revive Tibetan culture'. It doesn't take much imagination to realise that he made enemies. Conservative elements eventually forced his resignation.

Once again, the pendulum began to swing the other way and the bleakness returned. Wang was now in nursery and a happy and bright little boy who brought such joy into our lives. How is it that at one moment all is bright and the next, hope is extinguished? Our hopes were raised by the Democracy Wall only to be crushed. Hu Yaobang gave us optimism as he opened up debate and society blossomed and then he was deposed.

But my mind was on Wang. Suddenly one morning he had a dreadful temperature. I rang the studios and said I would be late as I must take him to the doctors. I never went back but instead entered the realms of despair. Our little son, our delight, died of meningitis on January 20th, 1988, two days after Hu's official resignation and three years after I birthed him into this world.

His little grave ... his very little grave ... turned my heart to stone.

Weiwei plants a seed in the dust

Each day, Weiwei looked anxiously into my dead eyes, afraid that my spirit had shrivelled and turned to dust with our little son. His way of bringing me slowly back to life was through art. One evening he said,

'Leave your coat on, Snowdrop. I've a surprise for you.'

We usually cycled everywhere so I was surprised to see a car waiting outside. I still don't know how Weiwei had organised it. It was driven by a *People's Daily* driver. Weiwei took his camera with him and winked at me,

'This is work.'

We drove west several miles and arrived at a warehouse-like building. Inside the surprise was waiting. Standing beneath *Book from the Sky* (Tianshu) in the China Gallery, I understood. It filled a whole room and was covered with calligraphy but all was meaningless. That is what my life felt like without Wang.

'Who made this? It is ... it is like a window on a new way.'

'You have read their minds,' said Weiwei 'The artists who work here call themselves The New Wave. I want you to meet the artist who is working on this piece.'

That was how I met Xu Bing. This work was to become the centrepiece of a new avant garde exhibition, on a much bigger scale than The Stars' shows. Next, Weiwei took me to see what the students were doing at the Academy. I was impressed by the discussion. They seemed to breathe new ideas; most were far more intellectual than I.

There was a temporary post available at the Academy and without telling me, Weiwei put my name forward. I went to the interview in a not positive frame-of-mind. When I opened the letter expecting a polite let down, my hand began to shake as I re–read every word over and over. I had been given the post.

That was how I once again started to give birth to works of art even though most of them were explorations of dark places. Weiwei blew on the little spark in me. It flickered more brightly but the shadow over me was not completely dispelled. I tore up my invitation to the tenth anniversary of The Stars, a show celebrating the spark we had lit. It was to be held in Hong Kong. But I couldn't summon the energy to jump through the bureaucratic hoops to attend. On the one hand I looked forward to meeting with The Stars who were now living abroad: Ma Desheng and Wang Keping from Paris, Qu Leilei from London, and the others would all be there brought together by art dealer, Johnson Chang. Because the Stars and the Art Movement had been one of the slivers that helped to wedge China open, it continued to be celebrated but I wasn't in the mood for celebrating.

My students were making waves, not me, but they said I gave them confidence. I loved teaching. What I most enjoyed was seeing the germ of a new idea and nurturing it. Sometimes students didn't see clearly that they were on to something. Once they realised they were being truly creative, that seed blossomed into a full-blown flower. I took pleasure in each achievement and so managed the occasional day when I didn't think of Wang. But then I was racked with guilt. How could I forget him?

Weiwei hugged me tight and said 'Snowdrop, we shall never forget him but he must become a precious memory – not one that destroys you. Paint ... draw ... create for him.'

I told Weiwei about the conceptual art that was exciting my students and it took him a while to say anything positive about it. Looking at my wedding gift painting on our bedroom wall he said, 'Your students' conceptual pieces may be good public art. They connect with the young but for me your paintings will always be what I love the most. I'll never tire of that picture. Remember the first night we slept beneath it? Come here, I'll remind you; let me massage you.'

And he did and I relaxed and massaged him and we somehow melted into each other for the first time since Wang's death. Weiwei made me feel alive again.

Beijing, February 1989: No U-Turn

One weekend, Weiwei and I went to visit the Godfather of Contemporary Art, Li Xianting. Despite his reverential title he hadn't changed much; he still sported a little beard and had the same expansive manner. His little courtyard house was a comfortable meeting place. It consisted of three small rooms with padded benches, soon filled up with artists who stayed for hours chatting. Old Li had cultivated not just Beijing-based artists but a new breed of artist from all over the country. The chat was the desire to bring freedom through art. The atmosphere was electric. The government had agreed that the whole of the National Gallery could be taken over for an Avant-Garde Show curated by Gao Minglu. The Stars only had one floor.

The symbol of the exhibition was to be the Chinese road sign for 'No U-Turn'. All the young people around me believed in the Beijing Spring. The atmosphere was filled with optimism and the belief that China could change and adopt democratic ideas.

Weiwei was anxious when one student waved his arms and said, 'We must wipe out tyranny. Those guys in the Democracy Salon talk a lot but we will act. We will show the people that we can express ourselves freely.'

Weiwei looked fierce. 'This is your opportunity to demonstrate that without street protests. Don't rouse people's emotions with slogans; that was what brought down Hu Yaobang. Supporting the student protests did for him. Nothing changes overnight in this country.'

Sara, Hu Yaobang was General Secretary of the Communist Party from 1982 to 1987. He was a reformer and had many enemies within the party so, when widespread student protests occurred across China in 1987, Hu's political opponents successfully blamed him for the disruptions, claiming that they were caused by Hu's 'bourgeois liberalization'.

From the black looks he received, I saw they thought Weiwei was a conservative and not what he really was, progressive but pragmatic. He desperately wanted those young idealists to survive and not to suffer Wei Jingsheng's fate. We sometimes met with writers of *Today* magazine, almost the only magazine to survive from those heady days. A few of us met for a meal and, as the Lazy Susan turned, the poet Bei Dao looked at Weiwei and, said, 'Wei Jingsheng was a friend of yours?'

'We were at school together ... until they closed. We often think of him. His sister has managed to visit him but he isn't well.'

'I had a visit from Professor Fang Lizhi'

Sara, he was a famous scientist and vice-president of the College of Science and Technology. He pledged to make freedom of thought one of the principles of university education and so had been dismissed by Deng.

'He's organising a petition of intellectuals. He has asked me to sign it and I will. It is addressed to Deng, asking for the release of Wei Jingsheng. He points out that most of his Fifth Modernisation *dàzìbào* is now party policy. Can you think of anything else we can do for him?'

We said we would talk to others and see if we could come up with any suggestions. Then the conversation moved on to No U-turn. We hoped this change in atmosphere could help Wei Jingsheng, make him seem less of a threat to the establishment.

The show opened in an ecstatic atmosphere. The National Art Gallery was transformed with long black carpets, extending from the street to the entrance of the exhibition hall, which bore the emblem of the exhibition. At every turn, I seemed to bump into friends, old and new. The whole place buzzed with excited conversation. I saw Shao Fei looking hard at an installation and waved to her, when suddenly everyone stopped talking, riveted to the spot.

'What was that? It sounded like gunfire.'

In fact it was gunfire.

Plenty of foreign collectors, academicians and journalists had come to see the show. Weiwei had been allocated to film with an American party. At the moment the shot rang out, some foreign newspapers had been interviewing the curator, Gao Minglu. Gao had, the previous year, scored a first, curating a break-through exhibition in San Francisco: *called Inside Out: New Art from China*. While in California, he had become friends with a Berkeley academic, an art historian called Patrick Newberry. I was impressed by Patrick's height, all 6ft 3inches of him. In Beijing he towered over everyone. Patrick was next to Gao leaning over him making an erudite comment on the show when the shot reverberated around the gallery. As we were ushered out of the building, I caught site of Weiwei with them and asked if he knew what had happened.

An artist called, Xiao Lu had called her piece *Shooting my own Art* and that is what she did – fired shots into it! I was a bit surprised. As far as I knew she had been collaborating with her boyfriend, Tang Song, making a sculpture. Full of rage, she had fired deliberately, trying to destroy the piece they had made together.

Sara, that day, I learned that one should not rush to judgement. The foreign press interpreted the Shooting Art as an act of rebellion. In a way it was, but her rebellion was against her boyfriend and collaborator, Tang Song! I am trying not to feel like Tang Song. Your refusal to speak any Chinese is making me angry. Your father calmed me down and said you will change your mind if I don't put pressure on you.

That night I shared a wry smile with Weiwei.

'Don't you ever think of leaving me – it's dangerous to cross a female artist. That gunfire today? Xiao Lu had a row with her boyfriend and they broke up!'

Weiwei widened his large eyes even more in a gesture of mock fear but then spoiled the effect by bursting out laughing.

The show reopened after four days but Xiao Lu was definitely the star of the show and that incident is what everyone remembers. I was only one of the female artists attached to The Stars Movement but it was harder for us women.

The next day I joked that Xiao Lu had fired a shot for women and this tall American who looked to me every inch like Gregory Peck smiled and said, in a heavily accented Mandarin, 'It looks like the world had better watch out. Once five hundred million Chinese women are on the warpath we shall all need to take cover.

I laughed both at his remark and his accent. But mine was a gentle Chinese laugh.

'There will be 'No U-Turn', that is for sure.' I smiled and Patrick said,

'Have you heard of Margaret Thatcher; often called "The Iron Lady"? She said "You turn if you want to; the lady's not for turning". If the iron ladies of China start turning, there'll be fireworks: Catherine Wheels?'

He laughed at his own joke and his laughter certainly made me turn, shudder even; his laugh was so loud.

Thanks to Xiao Lu, the show was closed. Patrick had come a long way to see it, so I thought the next best thing was to take him to the Academy and introduce him to some students and teachers. In the past this would have been a dangerous thing to do but there was a new confidence in the air.

Patrick jumped at my suggestion. 'Why yes, I'd like that very much.'

This tall, gangly, bespectacled man looked down at me but his eyes were kind and full of humour and intelligence; I liked him right away. Weiwei joined us and enjoyed his company and the night before he flew south to Shanghai, we shared a meal together in a restaurant near the Confucian Temple. Over dinner he wanted to discuss our afternoon visit to the nearby Lama Temple.

'I was surprised to see so many young people praying. I thought it was just preserved as a tourist site and that practising religion was banned in China.'

Weiwei explained, 'you're right, it's not encouraged. You can't become a member of the Communist Party if you're a practising Christian or Buddhist. But the country was pretty shell-shocked by the Cultural Revolution, the middle ranks more so than the peasants. Because of that, lots of people want to avoid politics and some of them have started to revisit ancient beliefs: Confucianism, Buddhism and Daoism especially. Most Chinese don't believe in a deity, so it is those three that most influenced us. As long as the party doesn't see your religious practice as a threat then it's okay.'

In the days I spent with him, my respect for Patrick grew until I felt rather in awe of this wise and knowledgeable American. I learned something new from him every day and I felt a wrench when he had to leave for the States.

Sara, it was Patrick who came up with an American name for me. He called me Winnie.

He seemed to sense my disappointment and said, 'why don't you both come over? It's easier now, isn't it? I saw some of your work, Little Winter, and I admire it. Why don't we try and put a show together? Your government seems open to that sort of collaboration. What do you think?'

What did I think? Sara, I was thrilled. The notion of seeing the USA thrilled me but it was an unrealisable dream. I looked at Weiwei. Patrick caught the meaning of my glance, and made an exciting suggestion to Weiwei.

'Why don't you team up with a director and see if you can get a visa too: Winnie says you're good with a film camera as well as stills. Why not make a documentary on the Chinese community in San Francisco? We have a large Chinese community. It all began with the building of the Trans-Pacific railway. Now that would make a fine documentary. I bet it could even be shown here. The government might approve and let you go. What do you think?'

I shuddered with hope. Maybe that would appeal to the government so that they would let Weiwei take big steps beyond our borders.

I couldn't wait to tell father. He surprised me by saying, 'I may even be able to come and see the show. There is some new electro engineering research that interests me, computing, micro-chips. Xiaodong, believe me, they will change the world. It will impact on everything, even art. You know I'm delighted. You deserve every success. PhaWi's (Patrick) idea for a film is interesting.'

Thinking of the railway workers, we began talking about how industrious our people are. For the first time since the death of Wang, I felt positive.

April 1989: Students foment change

Beijing broods; its moods are as harsh as its weather: dust storms, mud, rain and temperatures swaying from frostbite to sweltering heat with just a short burst of spring in between. The spring of 1989 was special.

On April 15th, we read, with tears in our eyes, the announcement of the death of the former General Secretary of The Chinese Communist party Hu Yaobang, who had, before his downfall, tried to liberalise the government.

Sara, you probably won't understand the hypocrisy in these words.

'Comrade Hu Yaobang was a long-tested and staunch communist warrior, a great proletarian revolutionist and statesman, an outstanding political leader for the Chinese army.'

The grief of Weiwei, Ba and I was genuine. We made our way to Tiananmen Square to mourn his passing. We imagined this was going to be so different from 1976 when the Gang of Four used troops to disperse us. Deng Xiaoping and all the leaders knew how popular Hu Yaobang was and so, despite his opinions being out of favour, they organised a State Funeral. They described him as a 'retired' official who had made 'mistakes' but praised him for restoring the political norm and promoting economic development after the Cultural Revolution.

In preparation for the funeral, on 22 April, I made a wreath from paper flowers. Weiwei and I left father with some of his friends near Chang An Avenue and slowly made our way to the Monument to the People's Heroes at the centre of the square. Someone hung an immense black and white portrait of Hu Yaobang on the Monument to the People's Heroes at the centre of the square. Approaching the monument we walked solemnly and laid our wreath beside all the others. The largest was from the students of Politics and Law University.

Tiananmen wasn't as full as it had been for Zhou Enlai in 1976 but even so the ground was strewn with paper flowers. For a moment, I stood still and saw my younger self with my father, amid that tension thirteen years before. That day of rebellion was a catalyst for change for the better so, unlike Weiwei, who was anxious about the mood of the students, I was optimistic.

More and more people came but I needed to go to the Academy. In those days, it was close to Tiananmen. I struggled to get through the crowds. My intention had been to paint some kind of memorial to Hu's attempts to involve the people in China's destiny. Ideas simmered but I felt drained and frustrated when they didn't materialise on paper. Instead I collected my bike and made my way home. Weiwei came home very late. I poured him a cup of calming chrysanthemum tea.

'The students are staying in the square all night. They think the funeral was muted and the government will try to bury his ideas along with his ashes. They want to draft a petition to Premier Li to give to him in the morning.'

Weiwei bristled with pent-up tension as he told me.

'They don't understand Chinese politics.'

I sympathised with his frustration. 'Maybe Li Peng will receive it sympathetically – if he gets it. It isn't 1976.'

'But they breathe ideals and ideals are not reality.'

'Hero, this isn't like you. You are sounding like an old soldier.'

'Sometimes I feel like one. Let's hope you are right that this is the start of something good.'

Oh Sara, that night was special. I am your mother; you will not want to read about our love-making. It will embarrass you. Mothers are not meant to enjoy that. It is important that you should know that when you come together with another human being and both of you commit yourselves with one heart completely to the other, it is beautiful – transcendental. As your mother, I hope you will come to know that and will not be satisfied by some cheap substitute. At least you will know that I am not cold. But I cannot think of that night without bitter tears.

The following evening, state television reported that the students at Xinhua Gate, the entrance to the compound where the government leaders live and work, had demanded to speak to them and, when that request was refused, they had attempted to storm the gate. On the screen were pictures of armed officers, blood streaming down their faces from cuts they said were caused by bottles hurled at them by angry students. Weiwei had heard a different story; some students had pushed and shoved, had been angry but not violent.

My students could think of nothing else but the events taking place a stone's throw away. One of them, Taotao, came running in,

'The police attacked the students at Xinhua Gate. They were sitting there, that was all, just sitting. They beat them using electric batons when they wouldn't leave. Lots of students have been rushed to hospital.'

A vision of my headmistress being beaten burst in my brain and the horror spread like lightning through my body. But I tried to stay calm and keep my students calm. Some rushed straight out to the hospital in case their friends were among the injured. The mood in the universities was like tinder.

On the 26th, Weiwei ran up the stairs with a copy of *The People's Daily*, saying, 'What did I tell you? This will get out of hand.' He threw the paper on the table. The party hardliners had attacked the demonstrators as conspirators who want to destroy the country. Since 1949, undermining any kind of opposition always began with a label.

You remember, Sara, how my mother was labelled Capitalist Roader? Labelling was nearly always followed by a purge. I decided to warn my students. This was still before cell phones and internet so communication was not easy.

Every day we heard stories and rumours, and could not be sure that what we heard was true. Being close to the square we went there often but it is vast and as the protest built, the groups involved became larger and more varied. I saw only a fraction of what was going on. There is plenty of film footage, mostly taken by foreign visitors and journalists, recording the events of those six weeks.

I shall write about it from my experience but I hope you will go on the net and watch the video clips for yourself, Sara.

The students were not afraid and reacted to the threat by going onto the streets. There were huge waves of demonstrations all over Beijing but the main one was in Tiananmen Square. As I walked through on the 27th, I saw that something was different; something had changed. The students were no longer alone – they had been joined by over a million residents and factory workers! In the hutongs, the lanes of old Beijing, not far from the Forbidden City, people were building barricades. I smiled as I saw an old man struggle to put a broken bicycle on top of a pile of broken fencing.

'We'll never let them in,' he said. How I hoped they could withstand army vehicles. Everywhere I tasted the hostility to the government; the streets were alive with protest all day and all night. The next week, Beijing echoed with meetings and discussions between students and residents and workers. It felt special to be alive at that moment in that city. From that day on, Tiananmen Square became a giant campsite with local people, including me, delivering food and drinks to the protesting students.

The atmosphere in the academy became more charged. It was a factory for making banners. Because of my training during the Cultural Revolution, the large calligraphy was easy for me but I let my students tell me what to write. It soon became clear that as well as wanting freedom of speech, the main complaint was about corruption in the Communist Party.

My students laughed as they dragged me with them into the square, which was a sea of waving flags and banners. Groups marching to the square from all parts of the city told stories of how the people had lined the streets and cheered them. Even when there had been police roadblocks, the numbers had been so large that they managed to get through.

The students vowed to remain in the square until the government would talk to them.

It nearly worked, Sara, but for two things.

A momentous visit was planned. Mikhail Gorbachev, the reforming President of the Soviet Union, was due to visit Beijing on May 14th. The government liked to impress important visitors with displays in Tiananmen Square. The students could not be persuaded to leave, and the parade was cancelled with the consequent loss of face with Russia and all in front of the world's press. I don't know how close the discussions with Li Peng had got but something changed after that humiliation. On May 20th, the government declared martial law. In the next few days the army was humiliated by the people. Two humiliations were a humiliation too many.

It was almost five o'clock and I was about to go home when I saw a military truck turn into the square and then another and another and another. All fifteen were packed with soldiers. I shivered, expecting the worst. I couldn't believe my eyes when crowds of people went up to the soldiers and tried to shake their hands! Someone said, 'A people's army should love people.' And it was taken up like a chant. When the procession avoided Tiananmen Square and turned north at Jianguomen, it reminded me of how The Stars had avoided confrontation. Then the authorities had saved face and so could compromise more easily. Could this happen again?

The uneasy stand-off continued like a piece of elastic stretched to breaking point. By then I knew the word surreal, oh yes, I knew about Dali et al. But during the stand-off, I lived it. I cycled towards the square weaving my way almost nonchalantly between the tanks while the students sat and ate and drank and acted out all the ordinary activities of life on this extraordinary stage.

Many students stayed resolute and vowed to go on hunger strike until the government talked with them but the groups from different universities were not acting in unison. Quarrels were pretty frequent. By May 27th, a week after the declaration of martial law in Beijing, the atmosphere was different. The student movement seemed to be losing some of its momentum as the government waited for them to tire and leave. Weiwei thought it could fizzle out like a damp firework.

All the people of Beijing and most of the country were looking to the young students camped out in Tiananmen Square for leadership. It was hardly surprising that, because of their lack of experience, it all spiralled into chaos for a while. Disputes and power struggles between different groups began to echo to the exclusion of the issues that had sparked everything.

Liu Xiaobo, a famous Chinese writer, was at Columbia University, and like most ex-pats, he was glued to his television screen watching the confrontations between the students and the government. He decided to rush back to Beijing and persuaded three friends to join him on a hunger strike alongside the students. He hoped that their maturity could help re-focus the movement.

In the meantime, something momentous was happening at the Academy of Art: the artist students had resolved to express themselves. They were not really politicians, but like the Stars, they wanted artistic freedom. At that moment of crisis, the students did something amazing that dazzled the whole world – they created a work of art that would shine like a beacon of hope. A student I recognised, I think her name was Mimi, said

'We must do something monumental, something new.'

An eager young man whom I didn't recognise joined in. 'I agree. We need something more spectacular than posters and banners.'

The discussion took a whole day but in the end there was excitement at the idea of creating a giant sculpture of the Goddess of Democracy. I watched, thrilled with what the students were doing and their determination to surprise everyone. That evening, I made Weiwei dance with me around the table. He swung me on top of it and cried, 'You're the only goddess I need.'

Those four days filled me with pride and admiration as I watched the brave students construct a dream out of styrofoam and papier-mâché. The government had its spies everywhere. The Security Bureau certainly knew what was happening and the names of all the students involved. Their vision was misunderstood. It was not based on The Statue of Liberty, as many think, but a piece of socialist realism, Worker and Kolkhoz Woman by Vera Mukhina.

Compare the facial features and you can see for yourself, Sara.

By May 29th, after the students had been working all hours for three days, the statue was almost finished. It was so large that it had to be cut into pieces ready to transport it to the Square. While they were deciding how best to do it, Mimi came running in.

'The Security Bureau has threatened the truck drivers. If they help us, they will lose their licenses.'

The artists were wonderful – so resourceful.

'No problem' said Chen. 'We can do it on handcarts; we are strong.'

He flexed his muscles and the mood relaxed as the girls laughed shyly. We hired six Beijing carts. They loaded the statue segments on four of them and packed the other two with the tools needed to erect it in Tiananmen. They thought of everything – even leaking a false itinerary to throw off the authorities - and moved three segments by a different route.

A sad sight greeted them in the Square that evening.

The numbers!

They had dwindled to less than ten thousand. The government was getting its way; waiting for the protest to fizzle out and die.

But Sara, The Goddess, like Nuwa swinging with her rope of clay, changed everything.

News had spread to the other city academies, and their students joined ours to assemble the statue. They linked arms around the carts in case the authorities arrived.

The Security Bureau called in troops to prevent the construction but the shimin, the people of Beijing, came to the rescue. Weiwei came to warn us.

'Everywhere people say they have stopped soldiers coming in singly and in pairs. The soldiers are not in uniform but the people recognise them by their army trousers and webbing belts. Crowds are acting as human barricades and hemming in buses loaded with weapons. But I don't know how long they can hold them back. You need to hurry.'

At dusk, the moon gave its light to the building of this new deity with a mysterious glow. The goddess was so large that bamboo scaffolding was needed to assemble it. I watched as Chen and the others climbed the fragile looking poles; they looked so small once the statue began to assume its grandeur. What an achievement - creating it in just four days and putting it together in this intimidating place with such speed. By early morning, before the forces could do their worst, the statue was ready for unveiling. It was positioned with care between the Monument to the People's Heroes, and the Tiananmen Gate where it faced the portrait of Mao Zedong. Seeing the ten-metre-high Goddess and The Chairman looking at each other eye to eye, I asked myself, 'Who will win this confrontation – the past or the future?'

Beaming with pride, the students decided to treat it as an exhibition and have an official opening. The statue was draped in red and blue material ready for an unveiling but who should have that honour? Two Beijing residents were chosen at random from the crowd and invited into the circle. The man and the woman were each given a string to pull and as the red and blue cloth fell to the ground, the crowd burst into cheers. The sound of, 'Long live democracy' echoed excitedly around that austere place.

Telepathy was in the air for soon crowds of people arrived coming towards us from all directions; more and still more and all of them wanting to admire The Goddess of Democracy. She had waved a magic wand and the meagre ten thousand had become 300,000, all defying martial law. My heart warmed to see the students' spirits revived in the glorious sunlight. And this is what they heard and saw – a statement written quickly and crudely on a long banner placed near the statue. A young woman from the Broadcasting Academy read it out to the crowd in beautifully modulated Mandarin.

'At this grim moment, what we need most is to remain calm and united in a single purpose. We need a powerful cementing force to strengthen our resolve: That is the Goddess of Democracy. Democracy ...You are the symbol of every student in the Square, of the hearts of millions of people. Today, here in the People's Square, the people's Goddess stands tall and announces to the whole world: A consciousness of democracy has awakened among the Chinese people! The new era has begun! ...The statue of the Goddess of Democracy is made of plaster, and of course cannot stand here forever. But as the symbol of the people's hearts, she is divine and inviolate. Let those who would sully her beware: the people will not permit this!

'On the day when real democracy and freedom come to China, we must erect another Goddess of Democracy here in the Square, monumental, towering, and permanent. We have strong faith that that day will come at last. We have still another hope: Chinese people arise! Erect the statue of the Goddess of Democracy in your millions of hearts! Long live the people! Long live freedom! Long live democracy!'

This document was signed by the eight art academies which had sponsored the creation of the statue: The Central Academies of Fine Arts, Arts and Crafts, Drama, and Music; the Beijing Film Academy; the Beijing Dance Academy; the Academy of Chinese Local Stage Arts; and the Academy of Traditional Music.

The students began to believe in their brave new world and announced the creation of a democracy university under the gaze of The Goddess. Classes were due to begin on June 3. But the goddess was the last straw for the hardliners. We needed to be taught a lesson.

The Goddess falls

If you have read this far, Sara, you will know that Tiananmen Square stages epic shows but the performance on June 4th 1989 was a tragedy that will echo through time. The Chinese government will try to suppress knowledge of it. That's not just a Chinese habit: all governments try to bury the past they don't like.

Government troops ready to move on the students were not local troops with allegiances to the residents and students. The Twenty-Seventh Army approached with tanks, assault weapons, and bayonets. Weiwei rushed into the Academy shouting, 'If I hadn't seen it, I'd not have believed it. On my way here, I passed armoured personnel carriers surrounded by *shimin* asking the soldiers what they were going to do with the machine-gun on their dashboard!'

The people's questions were answered with blood. It began to flow at 10:30 pm. Much of it was the blood not of students but of *shimin* who tried to prevent the army reaching Tiananmen Square. At 1.00 am, on June 4th, after a reign of only five days, our Goddess of Democracy fell. The destruction was witnessed on televisions in every part of the world. It's still up on youtube and was resurrected in Hong Kong in 2010 during one of its democracy campaigns. Like all goddesses, our Goddess of Democracy has proved immortal.

For those five days all eyes were on Beijing and the student protestors. No one who was there that day or who saw those events unravel on television screens will forget it. But papier-mâché and hope were no match for the might of tanks. The Goddess toppled forward towards the right. Her hands and the torch of hope were the first to break. The light had gone out. As a tank crushed our creation, it once again turned our dreams to dust.

In the Academy, we were unaware of the terrible slaughter on the streets of Beijing: the hospital near Yanjing Hotel was filling up with the dead and wounded. So when we heard the soldiers open fire in the Square itself, everyone screamed in disbelief. Weiwei alone was silent. He rushed to get the caretaker's cart and man-hauled it out of the side gate.

I ran after him. 'I am coming with you.' Taking one handle each, we headed straight towards the flames. The sight of the bodies and blood overwhelmed me with disbelief and horror.

Weiwei shouted at me. 'Get down, get away from the heat – her over there – let's start with her.' And so we lifted the injured girl onto the cart. Her face was red and black and I tried to stop her putting her hands on her wounds.

'The children's hospital's the nearest,' said Weiwei.

It was much harder pulling the cart now it carried its human cargo. It took us twenty minutes to reach the hospital. The noise, the sound of pain, the face of shock, the sight of blood and ... death ... death come too soon. Once we had found a trolley for our girl, whose name I shall never know, we left her and returned to help others.

Witnessing the massacre, Liu Xiaobo and the singer Hou Dejian tried negotiating. They persuaded the army to allow the remaining students to leave by the south-eastern corner of the Square and they agreed but too late for us.

We had already transported three casualties and were exhausted. Sheer tiredness meant our reactions slowed. Our eyes locked on an injured man and not on the soldier who had just shot him.

Sara, I can see that scene like a slow motion movie.

Almost without a sound, Weiwei slumped to the ground.

I screamed. I raged against heaven.

I kissed him. I tasted his blood as it dripped down his once familiar face onto my lips.

I told him to stay awake – please stay awake – don't leave me alone.

I begged him to stay alive.

I dragged him to one side and called for help.

I don't know who they were who came to my aid – not students.

Now it was Weiwei transported on that bloody cart.

At the hospital I glimpsed someone I knew ... Jia. Jia was working there! She too was exhausted but when she saw our burden, it was as if a bolt of lightning shot through her body. She rushed towards us.

Beijing, June 5th 1989

They removed the bullet from Weiwei's brain as carefully as they could.

Jia tried to take me aside to find a quiet place but that was, of course, impossible.

'They can't guarantee that if he recovers there won't be some brain damage.'

'What are the chances of him recovering?'

'Fifty fifty. Stay with him. I must help some of the others. We are all exhausted but if we don't keep going a lot will die who could have lived. I don't want to leave you, dear sister. I shouldn't. But take this, it's called a pager. A visiting French researcher gave them to me. If anything changes, just press the buzzer and I shall try to come to you.'

I sat by him for hours. I stroked his hands. I talked to him. I forgot to eat and drink. I don't know whether I was faint and delirious but I felt certain that he opened his eyes and said, 'My little Snowdrop ...'

I pressed the buzzer.

When Jia arrived, she felt his pulse, listened to his heart, looked into his eyes but tears flowed from hers.

'He was the best brother and I know – you think – the best husband.'

'NOOOOO. No. No. It's not true.' I shook him gently. 'He spoke to me, Jia. He can't be dead.'

Jia held me very close and we sunk onto our knees together and wept.

I don't remember how long we stayed like that. Tenderly, Jia extracted herself and placed a sheet over his body.

I pulled it back and looked at him. He lay serene, like a Buddha, but I was deranged, like a devil. Now when I think of him, it is that image that comes to me.

Jia drew me aside and said 'Go to your father, and together go to my parents, please. I am needed here.'

Part 4: DESPAIR

San Francisco, June 4th 1989

Patrick was glued to his television set on June 4th.

As the world mourned the dead in Tiananmen Square, he recorded the clips of the solitary unarmed figure of a young man confronting a long line of oncoming tanks. It was like the dance of death as they swayed one way and then the other to avoid him and then stopped. He told me, he cried. If it were written as fiction, no one would believe it.

In the hospital, despite my mind being on just one person, even I could see that more of the casualties were *shimin*, city people like Weiwei, rather than students.

Patrick watched clips of the building of the Goddess of Democracy. He had heard that students from my academy had created it and was concerned for me. He already had called some contacts about the possibility of mounting the Californian show for us and had tried to follow up possibilities for Weiwei, too. Earlier, in April, he had phoned about his progress.

'I should have something positive to tell you hopefully about getting your visas in June.'

It was June and, instead of the good news he anticipated, he watched with horror and disbelief as the dream of the people of China was crushed by the military machine. Film taken from a distance by a foreign journalist illegally recorded the Goddess's last moments before she was crushed to pieces. Anxious about us, he tried ringing. The lines went dead.

On June 14, he eventually got through to us. By then, my Weiwei was ashes. Patrick spoke sweet words of sorrow but I could not find the English words to reply and he then spoke in English, not trusting his Mandarin. He said that Weiwei would go down in history, as would all those killed as heroes, world heroes. My father took the phone from me; an anxious look spreading across his face. I heard him say something about 'fomenting counter-revolution' and Patrick said he wished us well and said goodbye.

All over Beijing in offices and factories, people were agreeing to say the words my father had, not believing them, but not wanting any more victims. China is an intensively governed country and Security Bureau officials were sent into every institution. Unusually, even some of those investigators tried to ignore tales of support; they knew how the country had identified with the movement and couldn't lock up everyone. They did just enough to put the frighteners on people. Silence helped us survive.

After putting the phone down, Patrick was angry with himself. Of course, foreign calls would be monitored! He was afraid that his remarks had put me in danger. He understood my father. He knew from the tone of his voice that it was a warning.

Beijing, June 30th 1989

I was still in shock when the knock came at the door and four policemen surrounded me and told me I was wanted for interrogation by the Beijing Security Bureau. I made myself take a deep breath and reply, 'Yes, of course, I will co-operate and come with you quietly but may I let my father know and telephone a lawyer?'

The answer was, 'No but you can call from our office.'

As they led me down the stairs, I noticed a neighbour's door close quickly. I shouted,

'Please, please tell my father.' The policeman guiding me looked angry.

'You said you would come quietly.' He nodded to a female officer and directed her towards my neighbour's door. My heart sank. I never found out what happened to her, this accidental eavesdropper.

I was not interrogated immediately but locked in a cell which was furnished with a metal-framed bed with no mattress and one blanket and in the right hand corner stood an enamel bucket. The floors and walls were all made from concrete. There was an air vent just beneath the ceiling and the cell was lit by a single naked light bulb.

That evening, I was bought a bowl of cold noodles and a glass of water. I tried to sleep but found it impossible as the light was kept on all night.

In the morning, I was given tea and a bowl of rice and allowed to the bathroom to empty the bucket and wash. After two hours with just my thoughts to occupy me, I was taken up two flights of stairs to a room on the top floor and told to sit and wait. It was furnished with a table and four chairs but this room had a skylight. For the first time in my life, I knew in my whole being, just how precious is natural light.

Time was already assuming new dimensions. I may have sat there for ten minutes, thirty minutes or an hour before a man and a woman entered and sat opposite me.

I asked if I could telephone my father. 'He will be worried about me.'

'Later. If you co-operate you may go home.'

They went through the list of bureaucratic information confirming my identity. The woman began, 'You were involved in the recent disturbance?'

'If you mean did I walk through Tiananmen Square when the students demonstrated; I cannot deny it.'

'You have an honourable position as a teacher. Yet you incited them to cause a disturbance. Why was that?'

'What disturbance?'

The man banged his fist on the table.

'Stop playing innocent. You know what my comrade means. Answer the question.'

'I have a right to a lawyer before I answer your questions.'

The man opened the door and summoned two officers and told them to take me back to my cell. As they locked me in I asked, 'Please may I have paper and pen?'

'It is not allowed here. If you are transferred to a prison, then you will be allowed to write and receive two letters a month. Those are the rules.'

For the next week, the pattern was the same every day. I was not allowed to see my father or a lawyer. In the end, I admitted being involved in the building of the Goddess of Democracy. They wanted me to implicate others. The woman said, 'It will be better for you if you co-operate. If you tell the truth about your husband's subversive activities against the Communist Party, you may even be able to go home.'

I hadn't been threatened with torture; I thought that could be because of my father's rank, but the conditions were meant to wear me down and they were succeeding. The boredom, fear and deprivation had gradually weakened my spirit. But the mention of Weiwei sparked the life force within me.

'My husband was a good man who never did anything wrong in his life. He died, was executed, trying to save the lives of your fellow citizens of Beijing, comrades who just want to practise freedom of speech, which is allowed under our constitution. My husband was a martyr.'

'Bo Xiaodong, you are charged with inciting the subversion of the rightful Government of the People's Republic of China,' intoned the stone-faced interrogator.

That was the most serious criminal charge – treason – whereas if they had charged me with causing a disturbance, the penalty would be to spend a year or two doing hard labour. As they dispatched me to prison awaiting trial, I knew what to expect. I would be joining Wei Jingsheng who Weiwei had told me was kept in solitary confinement but was allowed one visit a month from family members.

At first, I thought that I had missed my last two periods because of the stress and deprivation but sensitivity in my breasts made me realise that I could be pregnant. The possibility made my heart beat so strongly that I could hear it. I resolved to be strong for Weiwei's child. Weiwei would live in our child; our baby would keep the flame of love burning within me however dark the place of my confinement.

There was one prison guard who seemed more humane than the others and when she bought my meal, I intimated my suspicion. She arranged for me to be transferred to the Beijing Public Security hospital. I felt the first flutter of hope when my pregnancy was confirmed.

In prison, awaiting trial, I was allowed to have meals in the canteen with the other prisoners Slowly, I started little conversations but I had to be careful. I had acquired knowledge of the system in Chinese prisons from stories circulating among our friends when we had talked in whispers about Wei Jingsheng. I was a political prisoner so had to be wary. Prisoners convicted of theft, rape and the kind of offences that are treated as crimes in most countries, were selected to be trusties. 'Trusties' are used to report on 'politicals' and have free range to harass, beat and oppress them, too.

I asked every day if I could see my father. Then came the day they told me he could visit at the beginning of the following month. That day, they gave me paper and pen to write to him. My hand shook as I held it. How I had taken the ability to write, the joy of pen and paper for granted! Not anymore. That letter was so precious that I weighed every word. I spent a whole day composing my letter. I wrote a poem about my father. I wanted him to know how much I missed him and how I loved and admired him. I decided not to write about the baby but wait to tell him. Explaining that he could visit and bring food, I asked him if he could also bring a book of poetry and pen and paper. I had not yet been given a trial date. I hesitated over whether to ask him to make enquiries but thought the censors might reject my letter if I did.

Although the time spent in the dark cell was giving me bad headaches, the general improvement in my conditions made me feel more positive. My morale soared when I received a carefully worded letter from my father that he had received mine and he would see me soon. I crossed off the days until then on my cell wall. It is not until I spent time in solitary confinement that I realised how social interaction keeps you healthy. Rarely getting to speak to anyone, my vocal chords seemed to dry up. I decided to sing. Fortunately I had a good singing voice and if I didn't go on too long, the guards and trusties let me be.

Beijing, October 1989: My father's first prison visit

Sara, during the eighties, the range of choice of clothing made all women so much happier. Because we were free to choose, a lot of young people had become quite adventurous by making their own clothes. I enjoyed the western-inspired design with Chinese characteristics, particularly using traditional patterns and silks but structuring them in a more versatile way and mixing and matching with styles that were filtering in from The West. But in prison, it was back to the Cultural Revolutionary era.

I was glad there were no mirrors to reveal the awful truth. My hair was dry, my skin had no lustre, my nails were brittle and my shapeless prison clothes hid my secret.

I had worried about how I would look to Ba but in the end when he walked in, I had to be careful not to register my surprise. He looked so much older and frailer. He came in accompanied by not one but two officers. They sat on either side of the table, one next to me and one next to Ba. They were like physical opposites. One was short with sunken cheeks and looked as if it were months since she had eaten a good meal and the other was heavy and square and looked as if she had eaten for two. I stretched out my hand but the officer on my side banged the table.

'Not allowed.'

Father looked straight at me and his eyes told me the truth while his words were prison–speak.

'Thank you, officer. I see you are doing your duty. The young need discipline.'

The officer actually looked pleased with his remark.

'Xiaodong, I have bought you some presents and our comrades are going to see if the rules will allow you to have them. They say these warm clothes are permitted and ...'

I could smell something good. Oh, the joy of using any sense. Father uncovered a tray with food that, after my restricted diet, seemed a banquet but only just warm because it had cooled on his journey to the prison. Father was so dignified and in a voice that sounded sincere, he asked the guards to join us eating.

Prisoners were allowed cigarettes, even politicals, and another present was as large a pack as Ba felt certain would be allowed. The conversation began slowly. Each asked the other how we were and each of us lied.

'Ba,' I began but tears like needles pricked my eyes. 'I have some good news to tell you. I didn't put it in my letter. I wanted to tell you face to face.'

'Have you been given a trial date?'

'Not that I know of but I do have a date of a different kind. I'm pregnant, five months pregnant. It must have been that last night...that last night with Weiwei. Ba, I'll have someone to remind me of him, a little glimpse of Weiwei and I hope a joy for you too.'

Father looked at once pleased and concerned. He turned to the guards.

'What happens when my daughter gives birth?'

'She will be transferred to the hospital for the birth,' said the fat guard.

But the short one looked surprised by her answer.

'Ba, I know Jia and her parents will look after the baby while I serve my sentence. If they let me keep him at the beginning I'll be so happy but after that I don't want him to grow up in the prison.'

'Xiaodong, we should talk about that. I have spoken to a lawyer and the advice is that, if you plead guilty, the sentence will be shorter and easier to bear.'

'But Ba, you know I'm not guilty.'

'Only you can decide how to plead and now you have another life to consider. But I'm pleased. Of course I'm happy: what YeYe wouldn't be? I miss Wang. I miss him very much.'

The guards even looked moved when my father told them about the death of my little boy. From that moment, they treated me a little more like a human being and less like Prisoner X2467.

We were allowed an hour and the time like the food was being eaten away. My father didn't smoke but the guards and I lit up. They were not really allowed to smoke on duty and I thought more of them because they did.

'Ba, did you bring any books? It would help so much to pass the time.'

'They have to be seen by the censors. I'm sure there will be no problem.' He glanced at the guards for reassurance. 'I have brought two Dickens novels in English. Once they realise they are Dickens in his own language they'll let you have them and the War and Peace and the anthology which includes some of Chairman Mao's most famous poems, so you should receive that soon. Our comrades are here to oversee your re-education and will want you to read them.'

Ba's approach was working as our uninvited guests raised no objection when he broadened the conversation.

I asked for news of Jia and her family and my students. About the latter he didn't answer directly but instead said.

'You remember when you went to see some of their work in No U-Turn?'

'That seems a magical world from another time and place and yet it was only eight months ago. So you have seen some of them?'

There was a glimmer of warning in father's glance but not enough to cause alarm in our relaxed guards, as he continued,

'I'm sorry, Xiaodong, not your students, but do you remember the professor from Manchuria whom you met there? For the moment, I've forgotten his name but I shall be sixty-eight next month so can be forgiven, but you must remember him.'

'Do you mean when we were riveted to the spot by Xiao Lu's shot?'

The guard asked me to explain and I did and so she let us continue.

'He wanted to remind you of that and hope that it will not be long until you are back at work. You know he wanted to help you set up an exhibition. He'd been making good progress but that must wait. He wants you to know that he still respects you and is thinking of you.'

I tried so hard to control my reactions but I am sure that the guard opposite saw my hand tremble. I was not allowed to put them under the table.

'Your time is nearly up.'

I felt desperate. I didn't want my father to leave.

'Ba you haven't told me about yourself.' Then turning to the heavy guard said,

'Just a few minutes more please.'

She nodded: 'Be quick.'

'I retired last month, Xiaodong.'

'But Ba ... you loved your work.'

He closed his mouth slowly. I understood.

'What will you do with your retirement?'

'I'll read and play chess and, be warned, I may even turn my hand to art.'

The fat guard, obviously in charge, said, 'Your time is up. Say your goodbyes.'

Back in my cell, I choked back the tears. There were open bars in the door through which the guards and trusties kept an eye on me. I turned my back to it while I mulled over the news. How had father heard from Patrick? The only person it could be was Patrick. He must know I am a prisoner. The world must know.

The following day, a guard delivered the poetry book and the Tolstoy. The Government approved of Dickens but the censors must have been suspicious of the English because I never received it. From then on my mood was better. I gave myself a strict routine.

In the morning, I did Tai Chi and then read and learned a poem by heart. I bent over and with my finger made the shapes of the words in Bang Shu – BIG Calligraphy on the floor. I was determined to stay healthy for my baby. My human conditions felt better. I am sure that was because my guards were impressed with my father. He made it appear as if he agreed with them without saying anything that could worry me. He knew what news he needed to give me and how he could do it without arousing suspicion.

I was still allowed lunch and exercise in the yard with other prisoners. After that, I tried to nap, thinking that would be good for the baby. Then I would do some Yoga and tell my baby a story about his father.

And I grew. In December, they took me to the hospital again, they said for a check-up.

The hospital

I had to wait in a bitterly cold corridor for two hours before being shown in to the doctor. I was told to remove my trousers and pants and lay upon the couch.

My heart trembled at the sight of this woman. The previous doctor, a man, had been kind. This hard-faced woman looked like she despised me. I tried to think as my father would think.

'Thank you for seeing me, doctor. '

'Be silent. Just do I say ... Turn to face the wall.'

She left me like that for fifteen minutes and then returned.

'Lay on your back and open your legs wide.' I obeyed her.

She pressed her right hand hard on my belly and her left hand between my legs. I gasped in pain. 'You are hurting the baby.'

She slapped my face. 'How dare you talk to me like that, you ungrateful woman. You don't deserve even to be treated.'

She took out a metal instrument to look at my cervix and rammed it so hard inside me that I passed out. When I woke, I had lost my precious burden. I was told she had been still born. I asked to see her. They said she had been incinerated.

January 1990: I want to die

My hope disappeared with my baby. Sara, I wish for you, above all, that you never experience such complete emptiness.

I wanted to cry and not to think. I wanted to wash away the grief. But it was denied to me; my brain wouldn't stop thinking.

In the weeks before I sunk into that mire of dirty grey, each evening I had a moral discussion with myself setting out both sides of the argument. I was not really a political person, so I considered my father's remark about pleading guilty. I knew that if I showed willingness, they might charge me with just inciting a disturbance and if I pleaded guilty to that charge, my sentence was likely to be four years re–education through labour. If I was a model prisoner I could then be released after just two, especially as a mother.

Now I no longer cared if they executed me; I had nothing left to live for. My mother was dead, Wang was dead, Weiwei was dead and now my daughter was dead.

Father was allowed to visit for Chinese New Year. He knew about 'the premature birth' but not about the circumstances and the letter regretted to inform him that the baby was still born. As before, we couldn't touch. This time we looked at each other. Our eyes dead with despair but softened not stone hard because father and daughter looked at each other. I could see my father knew exactly how I felt.

'Xiaodong there is a date set for your trial. They say you may have a lawyer.'

'You know that I will plead NOT guilty. There is nothing worse that can happen to me now. Even death would be a release. You don't know how I lost the baby, do you?'

'Xiaodong.' My father's face froze staring into a terrible place.

'I'm sorry Ba. I am forgetting you. You shouldn't have to go through this with me. You should enjoy your retirement, laugh with your friends, not cry with your daughter.'

Father would not put his feelings into words with two guards beside us, only his eyes gave him away.

Beijing, February 1990: My trial

My trial audience was small compared to Wei Jingsheng's. And after his trial, they had tightened up reporting so much that it was harder for the West to get transcripts. They sent me a lawyer two days before the trial for thirty minutes. I decided that it would be better to speak for myself.

Judge Zhou Welin read out the indictment accusing me of fomenting disorder and counter-revolutionary activities, inciting the subversion of the rightful Government of the People's Republic of China. He asked me how I pleaded.

'Not Guilty and I don't see how the court can find me guilty on both accounts. Revolution has always been upheaval. Think of the Civil War and the Cultural Revolution. Didn't Chairman Mao foment disorder to overcome the bourgeois establishment? But I am not guilty of fomenting disorder. I would not know how to.'

The prosecution accused me of leading my students astray and creating the statue that celebrated our imperialist enemies. I answered, 'The Goddess of Democracy was not based on the Statue of Liberty but even if it had been, I understood that our leaders now called the Americans our friends.'

The prosecution described how the demonstrators defied our soldiers and refused to end the disturbance at the heart of our nation. 'The statue was provocative and defiant and led to loss of life.'

I replied, 'I thought the People's Army was meant to protect the people, not kill them.'

The judge looked furious and accused me of defaming our brave soldiers, many of whom had been killed upholding the law.

'Brave is a strange description of men encased in steel, opening fire on unarmed civilians trying to rescue the wounded. I should know. My husband was not involved in the demonstrations but took a cart into the square to transport the wounded to hospital. A "brave" soldier shot him dead.'

The judge looked incandescent and said, 'The defendant is abusing her right to self-defence. You will hold your tongue and answer the questions asked. If you continue to malign the People's Army, this trial will continue without you.'

It was obvious from the moment they arrested me that they would find me guilty; they wanted scapegoats. So I listened to their propaganda in silence. After the guilty verdict, I was sentenced to thirteen years re-education through hard labour.

If I hadn't shouted at the judge that they had murdered my baby, perhaps things would have been different. He ordered me not to labour camp but back to prison, for not being respectful in court.

Surviving solitary confinement

I was placed in a strict regime brigade, a strange plural word for solitary confinement. The gains of the last two months were lost. When they brought me food, I rejected it, I just wanted to die. Over the following week, I ate nothing but I did drink water. Children are not meant to die before their parents. Weiwei had kept me breathing but he too had left me. Inside my head, I inhabited one long scream. Was I losing my mind?

'I need your hands to stop me drowning. How could you leave me, Weiwei?'

Outside I heard some trusties laughing – no, jeering.

'What has happened to her pretty looks eh? Who would want to fuck her now?'

I resolved that from then on, I would not show my enemies how they made me suffer. I would not give them that pleasure. I owed it to Weiwei. I remembered his touch, his loving touch – yes, sometimes it was nothing but sex, but mostly it was more like tributaries of a river flowing into each other. What would he say if he were here now? I had an abundance of silent time in which to seek him out. He told me to swim and not go under. I breathed deeply and pretended to swim. I remembered how the water had released the tension after that teenage interrogation.

I began to eat and regained my poise through my own strict regime. After emptying my bucket and being allowed to wash, I began the day with Tai Chi but with difficulty in the confined space. For the next two hours I tried poetry reading and writing. I imagined holding a giant brush and writing Bang Shu. I gracefully stroked the names of family and friends and above all Wang and Weiwei on the floor and one in particular I experimented with was Pa – trick. A passing trusty, seeing me painting without paint, joked that Little Winter was a candidate for the mental hospital and laughed loudly at the prospect of a life sentence. She knew the truth about those places: if you entered as an offender, you either stayed for life or emerged in a zombified state. Next time she passed, I called through my cell door, 'What is your name?'

'Lan Chen. You know I am not allowed to talk to you only watch you. I must report your breach of the rules.'

'I was an artist, Lan Chen. I just do this to remember how. Look I shall write Lan Chen and try to bring in the rising sun. Are you a morning person?' (Chen means morning.)

She watched through the bars and after that was less hurtful in her remarks unless showing off to another trusty, and she didn't carry out her threat.

After lunch in my cell and solitary exercise outside in the yard for fifteen minutes, I read two chapters of Tolstoy. The writer's Christian socialism connected me to another idea. While an art student looking at Renaissance pictures, I had tried to learn a little about Christianity. Alone with my thoughts, alone because an oppressive authority wished to punish me relentlessly, I remembered how some orders of nuns have a vow of silence. They had chosen something that had similarities to my lone vigil. Surely this was the way to subvert their power over me – to live a little like a nun – to be silent voluntarily apart from meals and sing praises to God. I wasn't sure about God but I felt a spiritual connection to life itself.

Sara, the United States is a God-fearing country. I can respect that but I still have my doubts. With my Chinese inheritance, I find God a difficult concept. Since living in the States, I have come to appreciate the sincerity of most of the believers I have met. It seems to me they do try to convert their beliefs into action.

Father taught me Tai Chi but I liked the open air and some space to practise it. Because of the confinement of the cell, I soon chose Yoga instead, particularly breathing and meditation, followed by memory exercises in which in my mind I wrote letters to my father. I tried to vary the pictures I sent him. The lotus leaves of The Garden of Heavenly Peace, the taste of freshly picked bamboo shoots, my mother writing exquisite calligraphy on a fan, my father pretending to look shocked and him telling us the story of old soldier Wang, the swimming gang making waves, the sound of the skaters etching the ice, the rich red fields of Manchuria and the pristine snow in the silent forest, the Goddess of Democracy taking shape...

The beatings, the tanks moving relentlessly on and shots, one in a gallery and one in my Weiwei. I faced all the dark moments of the spirit except the death of my children; those memories I tried to bury. If they neared the surface, my pain was etched in every line on my face, Munch's Scream on the canvas that was me. I held clenched fists behind my back. No, I would not give them that satisfaction. I would survive. I pictured Weiwei looking proud and urging me on.

Sara, in China we say there is a poem in every picture and a picture in every poem. In prison, poetry painted another world for me.

My father had bought me a second book of poems and it passed the censors. The cover had a politically correct title and there was approved communist verse but there were pages of pre-Cultural Revolutionary work by poets like Lao She and even pre-revolutionary verse. There was one, which I believe was a translation from the English poet, Wordsworth, and another by an American, Carl Sandburg called Fog. I had this sneaking feeling that father had this book rebound and replaced pages with ones written and presented in the same style but not in the original anthology. When I was released, he confirmed that he had the help of a friend of mine from the publishers where I worked.

I tried to translate Fog back into English. I realise now that I got the first few lines right. And now of course, I see it almost every day.

The fog comes
on little cat feet.

It sits looking
over harbor and city
on silent haunches
and then moves on.

Wordsworth took me walking in lakes and hills, the most wonderful walks stepping out in liberty.

When we travelled there when you were twelve, Sara, it wasn't quite as I had imagined it. Although more green and verdant it was somehow made by man as well as nature. I had climbed other rugged mountains and swum in plenty of cold lakes and streams but I had never felt the serenity that I felt when I was in the English Lake District at Buttermere. But then you were with me and you had not reached the age when your hormones made you moody.

I ate my evening bowl of noodles very, very slowly, conjuring beautiful dishes in my mind. I cut carrots into flowers; I arranged leaves into still lives on a plate as I savoured every individual noodle. After that, I allocated entertainment beginning with a couple of cigarettes. (Under prison rules I was allowed to buy some necessities, once a month; cigarettes, washing powder and toothpaste.) While puffing away, I visited the greatest art galleries in the world and afterwards I sang and the sound coming from within me let me feel and sent me flying free beyond those oppressive walls. Some guards banged on the door and told me to shut up in insulting language but others liked it. They after all had to share the prison experience and if I kept it short it lightened their day too.

As a political prisoner, I was allowed a visit every two months compared with the laogai or petty criminals who received monthly visits. In April, instead of father, Jia came. We sat at that same plain table in the bare-walled room with the same companions but I loved seeing my friend's kind face. The gleam in her eyes had faded. Those days in the hospital had drained away her optimism. She looked ten years older. I didn't like to think how much older I looked. I asked about her parents, about her life. When I started to say the word hospital, I lost my composure. Jia saw my distress and understood.

She just said, 'We were so sorry Jie Jie. My mother, my father and I. You have suffered such sorrow.'

The guards looked uncomfortable. Jia changed the subject but I understood. For Weiwei's parents it was almost as heart rending as it was for me.

The baby would have kept Weiwei's memory alive for them too. That thought helped me. I shouldn't just think of me. There were others to think of too.

'I have bought paper and pens and believe the rules allow it,' said Jia, interrupting my thoughts.

'The prisoner has to exhibit certain conduct,' said Thin Number 2.

'We will consult the education officer. Next week, he will see if the prisoner shows willing to adopt right thought. He can order rewards for good behaviour,' added Fat Number 2.

'Your father sent a radio and some English textbooks. Have you received them?' said Jia.

'Politicals are not allowed radios.' said Fat Number 1. I had not heard of this and wondered what I had in store.

One morning I bit into a dumpling and it ground in hard pieces. I took it out to look at it. I had lost a tooth. I shouldn't have been surprised. The lack of light and the poor food were turning me into an old woman. I turned my back to the door.

The guard shouted to me to sit on the tiny stool and face the door as was expected of me. My confidence sank to its lowest.

I was assigned an officer to oversee my re-education. He introduced himself as Comrade Ma.

'I am here to help you.'

'Oh yes, are you going to get me out of here?

'Possibly, it depends on you.'

'If you want me to say I am guilty of wanting to bring down the state, you may as well give up and go, although a conversation is welcome.'

'It is all a matter of defining things correctly. I have read your files. I can see that you are not a committed political activist but you have been involved in some foolish things.'

'What foolish things.'

'Well, the so-called Goddess of Democracy ...'

There was something about the clipped way he said that that reminded me of another time, another place. I had learned in prison not to look the guards in the eye and realised I had not really looked at Comrade Ma. I had looked but not really seen. There was something about his eyes. Suddenly I was aware of the way in which he was looking at me – of course Thin Lips! A picture of the calligraphy on the wall when I was interrogated as teenager flashed in my mind followed by fear as I remembered his disturbing examination of me, intellectual and physical. But now he was wearing glasses. Something warned me not to mention that other time so I asked him a question.

'So you don't agree that democracy should be part of the constitution?'

'It is part of the constitution but you know that our priority is public first and private last. We have a different history to the United States.'

I was surprised at the end of the session when I realised that I had enjoyed my time with Comrade Ma. As a teenager he had frightened me in his role as a bully. But I steadied myself remembering the contrast between his manner, the threatening atmosphere and his decision to release me without a beating. Now even his manner seemed different, almost as if he was talking to me over dinner. He had got me to talk about my time as a peasant.

'You understand from experience that the conditions here are backward. We are trying to move our society forward out of poverty. In a country of almost billion people, we can't afford the luxuries of a rich country like the USA. There would be chaos.'

Comrade Ma's method was to get me to agree with statements he made. He visited me for an hour every fortnight.

He would list the party's aims and go through them with me. I found myself agreeing with the words. Thinking about it back in my cell, I told myself about the disparities between aims and words and actions. Most party members believed in the supremacy of the people. But what did that mean in practice? Political theory had been drummed into me, indeed into every person in my generation since childhood, and despite that, I really was not interested. I worked on a strategy that I hoped could help Comrade Ma and me.

'Comrade Ma, I have been thinking about your words. You have cited so many party resolutions and really I have not disagreed with them, so why am I a political prisoner?'

'I ask myself the same question, Comrade, but you know that I have to show that you have fully confessed and are on the proper track in order to recommend your transfer. Let us see if we can agree a wording.'

In the end, he came up with up a statement that did not refer to the events that led to my arrest and merely to incorrect thoughts that with the help of a re-education programme following the good offices of the party had shown me the errors of my thinking. I could serve the people better in an Education through Labour Camp.' He suggested I take it away and think about it. If I was able to sign it, he would do his best for me.

In the end, I thought who cares? The statement was ambiguous enough for anyone to believe anything. 'I'm not always right so perhaps I can sign this?' And I did.

In December, I received news that I would be transferred to an Education through Labour Camp to serve out the rest of my sentence. Comrade Ma came to bid me farewell and offered me some advice.

'You know if you receive good reports from your prison officers you may have the opportunity for release in five years' time. I wish you well, comrade.' I thanked him with appreciation.

We didn't have to think the same. He had helped me and I was grateful.

Education through labour

On January 1st 1992, I left my lonely cell for what I expected to be better conditions. I had heard of Tiantanghe Farm in Daxing District but, in my early privileged life, asked few questions about it. I thought that was it – a farm. It was not a long journey to 12 Weijong Road. The entrance looked clean and not intimidating and I was relieved that I was not being sent far from Beijing. Here I could still receive my bi-monthly family visits. The thought of father having to make the long journey to Hunan or Shanxi for a visit of just one hour had distressed me. I entered those gates in a fairly optimistic mood.

After a year in solitary confinement, I hoped to share a cell but it wasn't to be. By 7:00 am I was set to work cleaning the latrines and showers. Ten hours later, for the first time in my life I understood complete exhaustion. In pris-on, I had tried to keep myself fit despite being confined in such a small space but it is hard to build stamina in those circumstances, especially on meagre rations. I thought back to Manchuria where the work and weather was harder and remembered how Weiwei struggled at first, having come from almost a year in prison. Now I understood how strong in his mind he must have been because he never once complained. If I had a companion to complain to, I would have let it all out.

The camp had a factory and after a week, I was assigned to making toys. Surely I would get to know some of my fellow inmates and discover why they were there? I hoped that I wasn't the only 'political'. We were all seated in long rows and with sixty machines all whirring at once, the noise was too loud for a whisper to be heard and talking was forbidden. We were to make a batch of ten-thousand soft toys. We cut shapes from stencils, stitched the front and back together and stuffed them and sewed the gap and attached labels. They were written in English!

Sara, you argued with me when I didn't want to buy Mickey toys because some well-known firms sourced their Mickey toys from Tiantanghe. How can I buy products knowing they could have been made by slave labour? Sometimes money can seem like the real god of the USA, not Jesus who renounced wealth and power. As I am writing this there is talk in China of closing the Labour Camps. On that day we can celebrate with you buying whatever you like from wherever you like. We'll discuss the price when we come to that moment!

There was a short lunch-break of twenty minutes taken on the factory floor. I tried to talk to my neighbours but was ordered to be silent. Work recommenced for another four hours, with a five-minute break for latrines and a drink of water after two hours. I had learned to drink as slowly as a possible in solitary, to savour each drop, but here they gave you no time. If you slackened pace, they beat you with a fly whisk.

After three months, I was transferred to outside work and looked forward to breathing fresh air, seeing the sun and being able to move. I was ordered to carry building materials around the site and the task became more and more back-breaking as the summer temperatures rose. Most of the time, my mind was empty because my body struggled. At night, reliving each painful step, I remembered my gracious sophisticated mother and wondered how she had coped. I pictured her changed appearance when she came home from Labour Camp. At the time, I clung to the idea that she had survived but now I understood what she had suffered. Like Weiwei, she uttered no words of sympathy for herself.

In August, I collapsed while carrying concrete blocks and as I fell a block landed upon my right hand. I heard the crack and felt a searing pain, and knew in that instant that is was broken. They took me to the camp hospital for examination. Sure enough the doctor confirmed that it was broken and that I couldn't work but the hand wasn't treated nor was I given anything for the pain. The next weeks were spent either in my cell or in the kitchen where I was expected to perform tasks with my left hand.

I tried so hard to keep my fingers straight, it was only looking at my mangled hand that I knew what I wanted to do. An angry desire to make art consumed me. I confirmed a deep-set self-knowledge: sculpting, painting and drawing were who I was! They were the coming together of hand, eye, touch, and thought. I had been brought up not to believe in God but it felt to me there was something spiritual about my yearning. It came from a deep place and my mind was tortured by the thought that I would never be able to draw again.

The hand gradually healed but looked slightly clawed. I tried exercises to make it flexible. My little finger and thumb could move relatively normally but trying to get them to touch was painful. After all my losses, this seemed the work of a spiteful god. Why take away my last pleasure, my final hope? I felt an overwhelming desire to share my heartbreak with my mother. I tried to visualise her; her refined features and always neat appearance. But where were her mannerisms and the sound of her voice? I couldn't hear her. I raised my fists and cried, 'Why can't I hear her anymore?' It looked as though my enemies had finally won and I was destroyed.

Put back on cleaning duties, I was surprised when the routine was broken, and I was told I had an important visitor and was shown to a windowless office. The visitor was Comrade Ma. He stood up as I was shown in

'So Comrade, you are well?'

I held out my clawed fingers.

'I am sorry – an accident?'

His expression told me that he expected it was not an accident.

'I fell with a concrete block.'

'Sit down Comrade, please.'

I sat down but he got up and walked behind me.

I swallowed my breath as I felt a hand inside my shirt fondling my breast. I screamed only nothing came out because his other hand was over my mouth.

'Don't struggle, Comrade. You must know that ever since you appeared before me as a teenager in the People's Dictatorship Committee I have wanted you. Why do you think you went free then? Of course I knew you were as guilty as that husband of yours. Of yes, I knew him. I was the officer in charge of his supervision. I hated him of course but I am a fair man and tried not to let it cloud my judgement. Now you must thank me properly.'

He took his hands away

'If you so much as touch me, I shall scream I promise you.'

'What good do you think that will do you?'

He put his dirty clean fingers over my mouth as he squeezed my other breast till I thought it would bleed.

With that he left and left me shaking. I had thought I could not be brought lower. I did not want to live but how could I end this miserable, degrading existence? I lived in dread of being called back to him but his schedule must have been packed full because Comrade Ma was not my next visitor.

Instead, the following week BaBa made his September visit and he immediately realised something had happened. During those two years, he had been so careful about what he said and usually his approach had helped. This time was different. He shouted for the superintendent.

He drew his head up and stood very straight and with a cold anger, said, 'What kind of country is this? Why did you not treat my daughter's wounds? This is meant to be a socialist country where all citizens should expect basic health care.'

Sara, my father only knew the half of it. I was luckier than many in that place. I'm not going to write about all the things I saw and heard. If you want to know the truth about the camps, the Dua Hai Foundation will tell you but you'll find the information is so dark that it leaves its own stain. In a way I don't want you to know. And I don't want to tell it. I want to move to a different place in my heart, a sunnier, happier place. I want you to also live in the sun. Yes, I want you to be like your father and care about others, but I also want you to know joy.

I understand now a little more about how my father communicated with Patrick. No, not by email! As a prisoner, I was completely unaware of the worldwide web. The World Bank may have gone on-line while I was in the camp but a few more years would have to pass before even Patrick was emailing.

My father was walking in Beihai Park and stopped on the bridge to admire the lilies on the lake. He stood alone with his thoughts as people passed him by when he heard a female voice whisper,

'Don't look at me but follow me. I have a message about Little Winter.' She walked on as if a stranger passing a stranger, then walked faster and sat on a bench and lit a cigarette. As my father approached, she stood up but looked down. My father sat down and found a cigarette, which he put it in his pocket. He waited a while before leaving.

When home, he unrolled it carefully and read the note inside.

Patrick Newberry is aware of her incarceration and is campaigning for her release. Keep hope alive.

He was instructed to walk in the park every Friday but be careful not to arouse suspicion. If it was clear that neither of them were followed, they could exchange by hand otherwise, the drop point would be made apparent, as with the bench but not always the same bench, and not always a bench. Once she dropped the cigarette and father called after her.

'I think you dropped this.'

For a Chinese girl her eyes were large – she smiled as she took the cigarette and unseen, dropped it in his pocket. As they walked together for a minute before turning in different directions, he told her about the accident and the damage to my hand.

Sara, in the camp, I knew none of this. Ba's carefully disguised reference to Patrick had given me a faint glimmer of hope but if father had tried to tell me about those clandestine contacts, it would have endangered everything. I only learned the full story after I arrived in California.

California December 1992

At first Patrick had no idea how he could help me. He lobbied politicians and talked to Chinese academics and one of them came up with the magic name, John Kamm.

John was a businessman and vice president of the American Chamber of Commerce in Hong Kong, so an unusual human rights campaigner. It was John who convinced the majority of chamber members to pass a resolution condemning China's suppression of the Tiananmen Square protests of 1989. With his non–combative approach, John has probably helped more Chinese prisoners than any other person or organization in the world.

Patrick was able to talk to him on the phone and the conversation went a bit like this:

'John? My name is Patrick Newberry. You don't know me but I have heard a lot about you and admire the way you arranged the release of some prisoners in China. Can you advise me? I'm an art historian at Berkeley and a consultant on Chinese art for several galleries. I visited the 'No U-Turn' show in Beijing in 1989 and met a talented artist and teacher called Little Winter. I started to plan an exhibition, in California, for her and two other Chinese artists. But it wasn't to be. Her students made the Goddess of Democracy. You can guess the rest of the story.'

'Do you know where she is being held?'

'Tiantanghe Farm in Daxing District, Beijing.'

'I know of it. I hope your friend is strong mentally and physically. I'm busy right now but a colleague of mine is coming to San Francisco on Friday. She knows almost as much as I do. She is Chinese and managed to get out with the help of Operation Yellow Bird.'

'Sorry, I haven't heard of it.'

'Some Hong Kong businessmen set it up to help students involved in the Tiananmen protests to escape. Ting Wu was one of them. Meet her for dinner somewhere in Chinatown and I am sure she will be able to answer your questions even better than me.'

As Patrick said thank you to John Kamm, he felt more comfortable. He was doing something. He told me later that he had felt an attachment to me the first time we met and that fuelled his desperate attempt to help me.

Sara, you and Ting Wu have always got on. This is an account of Patrick's first encounter with her as he told it to me.

He was sitting at the table he had booked when Ting Wu walked in. He was not surprised that she was a singer in the Beijing Opera – at least she had been. She walked towards him with that assured grace perfected by performers and with a serenity that a life in music can give.

'Professor Newberry, I am Ting Wu.'

Once they had ordered and learned a little about each other, Patrick asked how she had got out of China.

'That has to be a Chinese story full of contradictions. The Hong Kong Stock Exchange raised $1,000,000 in a single day to pay the Triads to bring out those of us activists who wanted to escape. The Triads had smuggling routes, safe-houses, document forgers, and fast-speed boats to cross to Hong Kong. My companions were not moral men. They'd kill without hesitation for money but they smuggle for money and we just happened to be the goods.'

Patrick told her about me. And after a few seconds came a flash of recognition.

'Do you know, I think we may have met at an exhibition? Was her husband a cameraman? I recognised him from recordings for China TV. I never know the names of the cameramen but I remembered him. He had the look of a frustrated intellectual. Someone told me that he was shot; killed while ferrying the wounded to hospital. Anyway, what is it you want to know?'

'I heard that John has had some success in getting prisoners released and wondered how he had done it?'

'Yes, he's not the kind of man you would expect to be a human rights activist. That's why he's so good at it. He doesn't go in for naming and shaming and he made sure the government owed him big time.'

Patrick wanted to understand the background to John's success. Ting Wu said, 'What the Chinese government wanted most of all was to grow and develop the economy and to do that it needed to trade with the United States. It needed 'Most Favoured Nation' status and John as Vice-President of the American Chamber of Commerce in Hong Kong argued that they should have it.'

He asked if John could help me.

'I'll certainly ask him but I think there is something you can do.'

'Anything.'

'I understand that President Clinton is threatening to withdraw Most Favoured Nation status if China's record on human rights doesn't improve. Have you some political contacts? Can you get her name on the White House list? Have you heard of Wei Jingsheng, jailed since 1979 for putting a paper The Fifth Modernisation on the Democracy Wall? He's certainly on the list.'

Patrick set about doing just that, but he kept in touch with Ting Wu and followed her advice as he dared to hope.

Sara, the timing was perfect. What a game chance plays in our lives! I know it feels as if I'm trying to control your life. Having grown up in China when I did, I know the frustration that comes from not being in charge of one's destiny. Weiwei felt it and understood it much more than I did. It is hard to learn apart from one's mistakes but Sara, chance encounters in your twenties will face you with choices that can determine so much of your life journey.

At that moment, President Clinton was threatening to withdraw Most Favoured Nation trading status and the Chinese government believed he would carry out his threat. John Kamm was trusted. He helped compile the list of names and mine was on it. Patrick saw the Chinese Ambassador. He told him about the proposed exhibition in San Francisco before things got out of hand in China ... Oh yes, he was like my father. He knew how to phrase it.

'Little Winter is an artist not a politician; what good does it do your government keeping her locked up? Her talent will do the reputation of China good but her imprisonment will do you harm.'

He was persuasive. The Ambassador invited him back.

'Professor Newberry, I have good news for you. Your request has not been turned down but there are some concerns we need to talk about.'

The conversation was face-saving. It was not expressed as conditions but that is what they were and Patrick understood. They were prepared to release me into his hands at the airport. I must say 'Goodbye' to my father before my release and leave the country immediately. It was up to Patrick to arrange my visa. If the US government wanted my early release then they must have me. The Ambassador told Patrick to make an appointment to see him again if that was possible.

It took Patrick two months to arrange a permanent visa – a tourist one is easy– but an immigration permit is notoriously difficult to obtain. Patrick understood that statelessness can be a form of imprisonment; he didn't want me to exchange one dreadful life for another. The United States government may want China to free political and religious prisoners but that doesn't mean it wants to give us all asylum.

Eventually, by sponsoring me, he got what he wanted. The reason it was harder for me was another condition; my father would be allowed to visit me in the States so long as I refrained from political campaigning. But, for the American government, it could grant me asylum only if it was clear that I was a political prisoner. Patrick understood me well. He knew my father would want me to enjoy freedom and a better life but Father would be left quite alone and had always stood by me. How could I desert him? I was prepared to make that promise to the Security Bureau so long as they kept their side of the bargain and put no obstacles in his way. In the US, Patrick's diplomatic skills must have been outstanding to get me permanent residence.

Tiantanghe Farm

I was called from the factory floor and taken to the superintendent's office. An officer Liu from the Beijing Security Bureau was waiting to speak to me. My heart froze as I approached the door but the officer inside looked awkward, not confident at all as I entered the room.

He told me frankly about Patrick. I could be released at the airport and leave with him for the USA but I would not be allowed back into China.

'Your father will remain here. If you want to see him again, you must demonstrate correct thinking in the USA and not bring your country into disrepute. Do you agree? Sign here.'

'May I talk to my father first and then give you my reply?'

'I don't see any problem with that. I shall arrange for him to come tomorrow. He can bring me your decision.' He handed me his business card. It felt so strange looking at the business card of a secret policeman.

I was not taken back to the factory floor. I saw the officer giving instructions to the Superintendent. I was to receive enhanced rations and have an appointment with a dentist! Over the next weeks, I was not put to work and was fed well and I am sure drugs were put in the food because I started to look fatter! They made a denture to replace my missing front tooth and gave my teeth a scale and polish. They even arranged for a hairdresser to come and give me a professional haircut.

But that was after father's visit. He came in smiling from ear to ear. It was good. It was years since he had smiled like that.

'You have a good friend in Pa-wick.' Father never managed to pronounce it the American way but Patrick loved it ... 'I don't know why he has worked so hard for your release but I think you can trust him.'

'Ba, you understand that there are conditions?'

'Uh ha.'

'It means leaving you. They won't let me come back.'

'Little Winter. I am getting old. I will have no choice but to leave you and I don't want to leave you here in this prison alone.'

'Oh Ba please. You are all I have. You must live a long time. They say if I promise to stay on the right track, you can visit me. Would you do that?'

'What a silly question! Why wouldn't I want to see the USA?'

I laughed and relaxed.

'Thank you. You can tell Officer Liu, I accept his conditions. But please ask to see me again, before I leave. Ask if I can have my photograph album and Ma's fan to take with me to the States. Please bring me my albums with pictures us at the Summer Palace and at home with your books and in front of the red door. Yes and Weiwei and I, our wedding, of Wang. Please, I must have something to remember you all.'

And so it was arranged and a date was set. Father was allowed to visit one more time, bringing new clothes. The fan and the albums were inspected and I was allowed them.

Sara, I don't think I can write about how I felt on that last visit. In my stomach, I had a churning sick feeling of longing and regret that this could be the last time I saw my father.

We were still under prison visiting conditions but I broke away and hugged him. The officer shouted that the visit must end. He was led out and I watched him go with tears streaming down my face.

Part 5: EXILE

Beijing Airport May 12th 1993

You would think that I'd be happy just to be free. Life is never quite so simple. I was forty years old and had never been outside China. Although I had learned English and could write it quite well, I had very little experience speaking it. I had never even flown before and would be travelling with a man I had only known for two weeks. When he had seen me in 1989, even if I say it myself, I was physically attractive. I had been a sportswoman with a supple body but the last three years had aged me. My hand was still troublesome and I had no idea whether I could take up my career in art. To say I was nervous would be an understatement. To say I was afraid would be more accurate.

The officers had kept me away from the other prisoners: they probably didn't want the truth known but there is a surprising grapevine in prisons. The trusties looked at me knowingly, even jealously, through the bars of my cell.

The flight was to be early in the morning. It was still dark when the van left the prison with me in the back carrying a suitcase containing a few clothes, some books, the album and the fan and also some scrolls of my paintings. At the airport, the officer took me into the VIP lounge where Patrick was waiting. I had learnt the word debonair and liked it; it described Patrick. I learned later that term is dated but language time had not touched me. In comparison, I was self-conscious knowing how changed I was physically in just four years. He came towards me and bent his head to nearer my level and put out his hand. I shook it vigorously.

'I really don't know how I can thank you. I have nothing to give you apart from the few paintings in my suitcase.'

Patrick looked at the guard.

'I don't think you are needed any more. You can go.'

The guard objected, 'Not allowed, Sir. My orders are to see the prisoner onto the plane.'

Pointing to the other side of the room, Patrick said, 'While we are waiting, why don't you sit over there? You can see her from there and she is hardly likely to run away.'

The guard obeyed him; I was so impressed. In my head I was still a prisoner. Patrick was now in charge.

Patrick asked me if I would like some tea. Of course I said, 'Yes.'

While I was sipping the best tea I had drunk in three years, he showed me my exit visa and my American visa.

'This is unusual, Little Winter. They didn't want to give you a Chinese passport that you could use to return with. It was hard to organise things in the USA because you will be entering without a passport but this visa is special. I even have a letter signed by the President himself!'

I put down the cup and held it not quite believing what I was hearing. Doubly so, because although Patrick was talking in Mandarin, he speaks with a strong accent and I was out of touch when it came to conversation. On those monthly visiting days, I had either talked non-stop to my father or else struggled to find the right words.

'Why? Why are you helping me like this? Why is the President of the United States interested in me?'

'We have a long flight ahead of us. We shall have plenty of time to talk in detail but it is thanks to the President you are free.'

Tears always let me down. I began to cry. I can't really describe the emotion. It wasn't exactly happiness; I was moved and felt unworthy. It was like entering dreamtime. It was all so unreal.

It was unreal boarding the plane. Unreal were the crisply dressed stewards and stewardesses who greeted us and guided us to our seats. How clean the cabin smelt and how unbelievably comfortable after my cell! My life flashed across my mind as if released by a swift dragon. I felt uneasy. This was all a cruel hoax; someone from the Security Bureau would come on board, arrest me and take me back to prison. Patrick saw my body tense.

'What's the matter? Are you ill? Once we are in the air you can talk freely.'

'That's it ... "once we are in the air". Until we are in the air, I can't believe this is happening to me.'

Almost as if the pilot had heard me, the engines started up and slowly the plane taxied towards the runway. The suspense was terrible.

Patrick handed me a sweet. 'I like to chew on take-off and landing. Sometimes the pressure in the ears can be quite painful. It will be fine once we are cruising.'

I gratefully unwrapped the sweet and chewed it slowly as we rose into the air. I felt like cheering. For the first time, I actually smiled at Patrick, rather pleased that I had the denture.

Through the window, I watched as Beijing disappeared from sight and allowed my heart to fly free like a bird escaped from its cage. I suppressed an overwhelming desire to cry out. A sense of relief swept over me as I willed my paranoid fears to shatter on the ground beneath me. This was not a dream; it was reality; I sat back determined to enjoy my first flight. I mapped the journey in my head and traced it on the ground below. We flew south and east across the Pacific.

Sara, travellers often complain about in-flight food but after a prisoner's diet, I marvelled at the meal when it arrived in its little treasure box. I was like a child unwrapping everything.

Patrick suggested I try to sleep and then we would talk about the future. He showed me how to tilt my seat but I was too excited to sleep. The view out of the window was strange, white cumulus cloud under a blue sky. I laughed and my fingers felt the urge to paint.

'Winnie, you did tell me to call you Winnie? Tell me what's the matter? You suddenly look so sad.'

I held out my right hand and showed Patrick the claw-like fingers.

'I had the urge to paint that layered dream out of the window but my days as an artist are over. I'm sorry, Patrick, after all your trouble, I will disappoint you.'

Patrick hesitated for a moment. 'You misunderstand me. I wanted to right an injustice. I know there are many families suffering because of the protests in 1989. I wish I could free all political prisoners but I couldn't even have freed you if the President hadn't visited China. I'm not expecting anything in return.'

'So, how can I thank you?'

Patrick waved his hand in a sweeping gesture.

'I need to talk to you about what will happen in San Francisco. There will be press waiting, wanting to interview you. Do you think it best if I read a statement on your behalf and explain that I need to take you to a hospital to have a thorough check-up and only after that you will talk for yourself. What do you think?'

I was so grateful. I'm not sure I could have coped otherwise.

Patrick dealt calmly and efficiently with immigration and the press. He thanked President Clinton on my behalf and said I would speak to them in a few weeks' time but for the moment I needed to recover from a three-year ordeal.

Ting Wu was waiting with a car. It was reassuring having someone I could instantly relate to. Patrick said that he was taking me to a hospital near where he lived, to have a thorough health check. He would visit me and then we could make some plans.

Ting Wu said, 'Everything will feel strange at first. It will take time for you to feel at home. The main thing is to improve your spoken English. Patrick has arranged for one-to-one tuition. I'll show you around San Francisco's Chinatown. The Chinese have been here almost from the very beginning; Chinese labourers built the section of the railway going east through the Sierra Nevada. It's an amazing story. There was a race – another company was going West across the plains and somehow the two lines managed to meet. Amazing feat of engineering! You will love San Fran.'

I had a vision of Weiwei. I remembered his excitement about making a documentary on that story. Those embarrassing tears again. I choked them back and I'm sure Ting Wu talked a lot more but I can't remember what she said; her Chinese words comforted me but had little meaning for me in that moment.

Sara, I felt so lucky to have such support. That is why I have tried to welcome newcomers to our home. I know what a difference it makes. That is another reason I wanted you to be able to speak Chinese even though I also wanted you to feel you were American and not Chinese.

My first day I felt awkward; I looked so shabby. My skin looked sick and dead. But I revelled in new pleasures: the high-pressure shower and the Jacuzzi with all the gels and creams. I was given a sleeping pill that night and felt better for it in the morning.

They X-rayed my hand and arranged for me to see a dentist who said I could have an implant instead of the denture. I thought this a great idea but apologised as I didn't have the means to pay for it.

'Professor Newberry is paying for your treatment.'

With every day that passed I felt more grateful to Patrick but also embarrassed. That afternoon he visited me.

'How are you feeling?'

'Humble. You are doing so much for me and yet you hardly know me.'

'Look, if this worries you, once you are settled and working you can pay me back. But really, my pleasure will be to see you looking fit and healthy again and ready to work as an artist. The reports I have so far is that there is nothing wrong that a healthy diet and some supplements can put right except they are concerned about your lungs. They think you should give up smoking.'

'In prison, cigarettes were the breath of life: even in solitary, they were allowed. I'll try to reduce. Weiwei got me in the habit. That's how he coped with frustrations.'

'I hope your father told you how sorry I was about the loss of Weiwei. I liked your husband. He was a brave man. I also heard about the baby.' He hesitated 'I was afraid for your mental health but I'm amazed that you seem to be extraordinarily sane.'

'Well, thank you. Did you expect me to be banging my head on the wall?'

'I wouldn't have blamed you if you did. That response just now – you have kept your sense of humour after all you have been through. Ting Wu is coming tomorrow and will take you shopping for everything you need. At the weekend, she would like to take you to a health farm. She thinks you will come out looking much more like your old self and feel confident when I take you to see our art students.'

'I do like her. Thank you, Patrick, for everything. You know the only thing that concerns me is my father. Do you think I can phone him? Oh, and what do they grow on a health farm?'

'Your father! But of course, why didn't I think of that? It will be best to phone from my house and,' he looked a little embarrassed, 'here's a leaflet about the health farm.'

I looked even more embarrassed than him and he asked 'Is there something wrong?'

'You have thought about just about everything. I don't know how I can thank you.'

A few minutes of silence passed before he said, 'We must think about where you will live. My house is quite large and you are welcome to come home with me until you have built a life of your own.'

'Oh Patrick. Yes, please. I can't wait to see your house. It must be full of great art.'

'I'll enjoy showing you around. I must get back to work now, but I'll see you on Sunday. Ting Wu will deliver you to my door. You will need to come back here as an out-patient; they think they can help a little with the hand. Here is the report – they say it has healed reasonably well, all things considered. You must have worked at it. There is a little loose cartilage they can remove but otherwise, it will be physio. It won't ever be quite the same as before, and they are concerned that arthritis may set in, but in the meantime they think you will adapt it to normal use. Yes – including being able to paint. There are other kinds of art I want to show you. It will be interesting to see your reaction.'

So Sara, a rather more stylish and glossy Little Winter, now Winnie, arrived at his house that Sunday. Ting Wu took me shopping on the Saturday and you know yourself what a great eye for fashion she has.

I was seeing shops packed with consumer goods for the first time. The choice of goods for sale in Beijing was vast compared with the time of the Cultural Revolution but the shops in San Francisco were like seduction. I couldn't have imagined so much for sale and blazing with colour. Everywhere was sparkling clean. In Berkeley – you won't be surprised – the bookshops and galleries were my magnet; I just couldn't wait to lose myself in them. But Ting Wu said I should do that on my own. She was right because, after the hair stylist and skin treatments, the aromatherapy massage was wonderful. It was the first time I had experienced the joy of touch since Weiwei was killed. I emerged like a summery version of Little Winter moulded by the Goddess Nuwa. But I felt the load of debt to Patrick growing as the bills must have flooded in.

The press conference

'Father? Is that really you? How are you? Are we being heard?

'It is so good to hear from you. Tell me about you.' Ba replied.

I told him what I felt I could, considering the clicks on the line meant someone was listening in. I wanted Ba to be able to come to California. I didn't want to risk saying anything that could jeopardise that possibility so our conversation was a bit stilted. At least I sensed some of his old energy and the warmth in his voice. I can't begin to describe the dreamlike experiences and impressions of those first weeks leading up to the proposed press conference.

Patrick warned me, 'They will want to talk about the Tiananmen Massacre so let's work out a response that may not alienate Beijing – at least not too much.'

The press conference was to take place at the theatre in the university. I was overwhelmed by the number of journalists and television cameras all looking at me. I was glad of my make-over.

'Miss Bo, what are your impressions of California?'

'Sunny! And the welcome has been as warm as the weather.'

'You speak English. How is that?'

'Thanks to my father. After President Nixon visited China, learning English was encouraged but the teaching aids were not available. Somehow my father managed to get a dictionary for me. I taught myself and then as Deng Xiaoping's influence grew I learned pwoperly part-time in the University. Sowwy if you have pwoblems understanding me – I learned to write well but to speak is hard for me. I had little chance to practise in prison.'

'No problem. Miss Bo. We understand your students were among those who built the Goddess of Democracy. Can you tell us about it?'

'Professor Newberry has told me that in the USA most people think it was modelled on the Statue of Liberty but that wasn't the only influence. You won't be surprised that the students were more aware of revolutionary Russian art than Western art. They knew Vera Mukhina's Worker and Kolhkoz Woman. All those images came together in the passion of the moment. Whatever the influences, it was intended to be an inspiring symbol and it was.'

'Do you know what has happened to your students?'

'I was arrested soon after the ... Professor Newberry and Ting Wu of the Dui Hua Foundation can tell you more than me. A friend visiting me in prison – we were never alone, you understand – mentioned some names and I got the impression that most had returned to college but were subdued.'

'That brings us to your experiences. How were you treated? I understand you lost a baby?'

I must have looked visibly shaken. It seemed such a personal question for the TV. Patrick intervened, 'Winnie wants to put the past behind her. I have some good news to announce. Next year, she will participate in an exhibition of three Chinese artists, she being the third. I'll provide you with more information in due course. Thank you, ladies and gentlemen. We appreciate your interest and support. If you want to know more about the Dui Hua Foundation, Ting Wu will take your questions.'

Once back at the house, I tackled Patrick about his announcement. The exhibition was news to me and I really didn't feel up to it.

'Winnie, I know you can do it and you'll feel better if you can start work and earn some money. A stunning exhibition will kick-start your career.'

'Patrick, I haven't worked for three years and before that I was not producing anything exceptional. You don't know about Wang, my little boy ...'

'Let me get you a drink and why don't you tell me everything?'

We talked. No, I talked for hours. And then I wept for Wang. And I wept for Weiwei. And I wept for my dead baby daughter and Patrick took me in his arms and I let myself melt. As his face dissolved into a youthful soft version of the features I have come to love, he murmured,

'Winnie, thank you ... Winnie ...' and he laid his head contentedly on my breasts and closed his eyes. I was thanked by this kind man to whom I owed so much that all thanks were insufficient. And in that moment, I was re-born. I was the American Winnie, living my new life, the misery of Little Winter left behind in Beijing.

Sara, not many people know the exact day their baby was conceived but I do. After everything, I thought I was barren. Of all of Patrick's gifts, you were the most wonderful, the most unexpected. You gave me back my life, my inspiration, my career.

I love you and I love your father. Patrick taught me so much about love. I initially fought against it because Patrick wasn't Weiwei. I found my growing fondness for him confusing. That blossomed into a mature love, not the galloping passion of youth but the thoughtful revelling in his being. I needed to give love. You would be drowned by it but Patrick grew as a man because of it.

But what an ungrateful wretch I was the next day!

'Patrick, what did you mean committing me to an exhibition? Look at this.' I waved my damaged right hand in his face. 'How can I paint with this?'

Completely unfazed he said, 'I have some meetings this morning, but come to my office at 2pm and I'll show you things which will change your mind.' With that he walked out without saying goodbye.

Despite my rebellious mood, I agreed. Taking my time, I walked to the campus, stopping at some bookshops on the way. Each time, I browsed through the art books and found myself looking at work quite off my radar. China had freed up a lot in the eighties so I had seen works by Picasso, Henry Moore, Barbara Hepworth, Andy Warhol, Mark Rothco but not Jackson Pollock, or graffiti.

I was already feeling ashamed of myself when I walked into Patrick's office. His secretary was there and I didn't want to make a humiliating apology in front of her.

'Have you eaten?'

'No, but it's all right.'

'No it isn't ... I'm taking you to the canteen, but bring these catalogues.'

As we sat down to eat, he said, 'Do you remember our discussions after 'No U-Turn' ... when I described your Great Wall piece as conceptual? There is something unusual stirring in England. A collector called Charles Saatchi is patronising some way-out stuff. Look at this one.' He handed me a new catalogue entitled: Young British Art: Damien Hirst, Sarah Lucas, Mark Wallinger and Rachel Whiteread. 'Look Winnie, I'm not asking you to paint. But you've a lot of work to do to catch up and discover what's new. You're in the USA now. Sure, you're purist at heart but the market drives Western art. You'll learn to understand that too. You must attract a distinguished collector. You've ideas and that's what matters. You can use other people to help you execute them but for that, you have to think BIG.'

'Patrick, I'm so sorry. You must think me ... how do you say it? An ungrateful bitch? Shut away for three years, I lost confidence. How much time do I have?'

From then on, every spare moment, I visited artists and galleries and mixed with the fine art students to feel my way into the atmosphere of the time. But I was determined not be financially dependent on Patrick and discussed with him how I could earn a living in the meantime.

'Easy,' he said. 'Teach Mandarin or translate it. Business with China shows no sign of slowing down.' He was right, as always. The demand for Mandarin classes had risen so I began to do some tutoring and gradually started to pay my way. Then I missed my period.

When I missed my period, Sara, I didn't immediately think I was pregnant. I thought permanent damage was done and that was it, I could have no more children. I assumed it was early onset menopause – until that is I was sick in the mornings.

So many emotions! So many questions! How would Patrick feel about it? He was over fifty and perhaps didn't want children? I loved Patrick's beautiful home but would he want a child shattering his peaceful life and his precious things? The night after I tested positive, I cooked a banquet for us. As we toasted each other and our life together, I silenced him with a kiss and said,

'Patrick, it is three lives ...How do you feel about that?'

I thought he was going to cry.

'Winnie, Winnie, come here you wonderful, beautiful, every stunning adjective going. You can't know how happy you have made me.'

For once my tears were of joy. He lifted me up quite easily and swung me around.

'Do you know how happy you have made me, my miracle worker? You miraculously deliver me from prison and now you have given me a gift so precious that I can't find words to express my feelings. I thought this new life could never happen. I'll cherish you and our baby for as long as I live.'

As he stroked my hair and lifted my chin, he said,

'There are things you need to know about me. You see me swanning around with the bright young artists but actually, I'm an old-fashioned man. Look, I'm a Professor of Art History not a bohemian in a garret and I want my child to feel secure. Will you marry me, Winnie? Do say you'll marry me.'

Sara from the moment you were conceived, everything about my life became happier. After Weiwei was killed, I vowed never to paint humans again. They were too cruel. The moment you were born I fell in love with you and I painted you and I modelled you. You know only too well, you always complain about all my baby stuff being embarrassing: that there is too much of you as a naked baby.

The date was set and Patrick arranged a three-month tourist visa for my father to come to the wedding. I'm not normally superstitious but I felt like pinching myself because everything was going too smoothly; I didn't believe it could last.

Sara, I'm embarrassed to tell you but I even consulted a woman in Chinatown. You'll say I'm a hypocrite because, like my father, I told you that sort of thing is a silly superstition. In fact Sara, I often tell you to do as I say when I should set

a better example. I have wanted you to grow up as the all American girl without the complications of knowing about my Chinese life and yet I insisted on you learning Mandarin.

My excuse for my lapse into superstition is that a good mood is worth having and I was so happy when the astrologer said my cycle of good luck would last. And she was right; there was no problem. Just like that, they gave Father a passport. My wonderful kind father was coming to California to see me married and would be here for the birth of his grandchild!

Even within the womb, you unleashed creativity in me. Patrick made me a studio for painting in our home but he introduced me to Ange and Shuyun, two Chinese-American artists and I began to work on larger projects in their studio. Patrick worked hard to plan the joint exhibition; the only problem was the timing: to arrange it before or after you were born? In the end we chose ten months after your due date for our show. We played around with possible titles and decided on Chinese Sensations. Each new dawn, I awoke in a cloud of happiness. I couldn't wait to start work; my confidence was growing as you were growing within me.

Berkeley April 1994

Sara, you have seen the pictures; we were married in The Claremont in Berkeley with its stunning views over San Francisco Bay.

The eighty guests were mostly Patrick's friends and colleagues and those artists I had come to know and like. One very special person gave his approval, my father. Ting Wu was my matron of honour and she sang at our wedding and chose a song especially for him from *Liang Shan Bo* and *Zhu Yingtai*, a Chinese version of *Romeo and Juliet.* Chinese men are not good at showing their emotions but Father was so delighted, he stood up and applauded and applauded and she came over and bowed deeply to him and he loved it.

Father had bought a present from Jia.

'She says she knows you will never forget Weiwei but wishes you good fortune and happiness with Patrick.'

On unwrapping, the elegant vase decorated with the calligraphy for good luck and happiness in perfect brush strokes, my tears were a flood of relief. Jia was like a sister to me and I worried that she might think I was betraying her brother's memory by marrying Patrick. Caressing the smooth porcelain, I felt healed.

I was six months pregnant with you and we made no attempt to conceal it but lots of the wedding photographs are head and shoulders or else I am sat behind the dining table. Take a look at your father at how proud he looks in the ones standing by me; my shape seemed to reflect the curves of Jia's vase.

I thought of Patrick as some kind of magician: he managed to get my father's visa extended for a further three more months. He was shown around the engineering department and excited by what he saw but learning English at his age was hard. He returned to Beijing with photographs of the wedding and of him proudly holding his grand–daughter.

Look at the delight on his face holding you for the first time. How can I describe my feelings; I'm an artist not a poet and you don't like the way I've shown it.

You slipped out of me trying to swim like a wet fish beached on the shore. Panicking in your dry new world, you let out a piercing scream. I clasped you close to me and you lay softly on my breast as if you were part of me. Then I handed you to your father and you do not need me to tell you how much he adores you and always will. That is the best I can do in words; I can express it better in art. I am in my element in water and on ice and *Waterbaby* and Beached were inspired by your birth and they were part of the exhibition that made me start to feel that I belonged in this society. Lots of mothers spoke to me saying how they loved them and how they captured that strange moment of birth. But I am skipping ahead.

Sara. I found it hard letting you out of my sight but the day care at Berkeley was wonderful and not far from the studio. You couldn't seem to wait to explore the world and liked the stimulation.

At ten months old you were witness to my first exhibition, *Chinese Sensations.* James Hirsch was among the crowd at the preview. I had expanded my methods thanks to Patrick and the influence of my fellow artists but I like to think I bought together Eastern and Western styles and used traditional methods within conceptual art. *Mountains and Valleys of the Mind* was Chinese brush work. The workshop cast a giant head for me but behind the eyes set within the brain was my Chinese landscape painting, with symbolic mountains and rivers. Once I started painting, I couldn't stop despite my damaged hand. I just changed my style: my strokes were cruder but also bolder.

Traditional Chinese folk stories resonate with me and my favourite is the myth of the Goddess Nuwa creating humans in her image. I used this subversively. In order to obtain my released from prison, I had promised that

I wouldn't campaign politically in the West and I'd kept my word because I wanted to maintain contact with father. But when Patrick took me to Los Angeles to see the replica of the Goddess of Democracy made in honour of the students, I felt so close to those days in Tiananmen. I mourned the dead, I mourned Weiwei and anger welled up and washed over me threatening to make me renege on that promise.

But I listened to Patrick and my political pointers were subtle. My Nuwa was huge and I used the same materials and methods that my students had used to make the Goddess of Democracy and her arm is outstretched just as hers was, and at the end of the clay-tipped rope, new life. You could read it how you liked, literally the creation story or new politics but that was in the eye of the beholder.

Sara, you should know that the face of Nuwa was that of my own mother. It was my way of thanking and honouring her.

My other conceptual piece was *Shoes*. In China, small feet are laden with symbolic and erotic overtones. My grandmother, like most prosperous Chinese women of her day, had bound feet. The revolution was mostly good for women in the early years, and it outlawed that barbarism of controlling women. But in China, even today, if you threaten the dynasty they will see that you are kept in *small shoes*. I created the work Shoes for Weiwei, his gifts frustrated by constraint and monitoring. So I selected shoes like the running shoes that give you speed, and erotic stilettos that confine but have sexual overtones. I lined these up with Wellington boots and skates and sandals granting freedom to move in different elements. Then I made them in smaller and smaller sizes, finishing with a model of bound feet in Chinese silk slippers.

After *Shoes* came *Waterbaby*, *Beached* and *Mother and Child* which I painted in traditional Chinese brushwork. The subject matter was Western but the technique and colour Chinese. I was attracted and repelled at the same time by a lot of the conceptual art I was seeing. I admired the ideas and the execution but felt something profoundly disturbing when those ideas were like icy intellectualisms without emotion, devoid of sensuality or humanity. I knew I wanted both, just as I desired to find a way of bringing East and West together.

I was overwhelmed by the response to that show in the media and from the people who came to see and to buy. James Hirsch bought *Nuwa*. You know that, in 2006, in my Los Angeles show, he bought *Clouds over Beijing* for a record sum. Thanks to him and the freedom and confidence his support has given me, prompted by Patrick, I have the time and money to spend on expressing myself in words for you.

Sara if you have managed to read this far, you will understand the miracle that you are to me, the unbelievable beauty. The best and worst of times seem to sneak up unawares and take you by the throat. When we sit down together to watch a Chinese film you nearly always joke, saying, 'So Mum, who dies tonight – the heroine, the hero or both?'

But this news is the stuff of melodrama. I should have listened to you. You nagged me enough times about it. I tried to give up smoking but not hard enough. I didn't puff as many as Weiwei: they were his way of coping with his frustrations. In prison smoking helped me survive. When you read this, you will remember this day, the day I received the results of my biopsy. I have a 50 /50 chance. Jia once said the same about Weiwei.

Sara, they will operate on the January the nineteenth. In the next three days, I shall try to focus on my story and get as far as I possibly can. When I began to write for you – I thought of it as a series of letters but it has turned into a book and now I'm in a desperate race to finish it. How I wish I'd listened to Patrick when he first suggested writing my memoir.

Berkeley, February 1st 2011

Sara, I want so much to write about you growing up but I may only have two or three months left and I can't write five hundred words a day from now on. I return to my original idea of writing you letters. It seems more immediate, like an intimate conversation rather than a memoir at arm's length. Like the memoir, these letters are wholly for you.

My battles have been with ideas and with humans who wanted to harm me because of those ideas. My battleground has been ideas of freedom and dignity and respect. I could never be defeated because I hung on to the memory of what it means to be loved. Love saw me through the darkest moments. But I am losing this present battle. There is a stranger within my body, eating me bit by bit, soon to savour victory. Those little friends, the cigarettes that helped me through my ordeals, are taking their revenge. I so wanted to finish writing my memoir for you but I'm struggling. Since your birth, I have kept an album about you adding to it almost every precious month. As well as photographs and examples of your writing and art, there are my sketches of you and your friends. They will remind you of good times. A little of me lives on in them as I do in you.

Don't feel sorry for me. I thought that I would die in prison. I was desperate to escape the misery of all the people I loved who were taken from me. At that time, I could not have imagined the happiness and fulfilment that you and Patrick have given me. I have been lucky beyond compare these past 17 years. I have seen more of the world than most people, great works of art and beauty, made treasured friends and had many, many good times. Thanks to Patrick I have grown as an artist and as a human being. These years were unasked for and unexpected, and I am blessed to have received them. Our love came unexpectedly into his life and sometimes he will be lonely. Look after him for me. The best joy you can give him will be to let him see you fulfil your dreams.

X Your Mother

February 19th 2011

Dear Sara,

I can't imagine better news. Jia will shine a light on my last months. Jia is coming as a visiting Professor of Medicine at Stanford. You will have an Auntie who will love you because you are my daughter. I know you will love her as much as I do. She is such fun. Her visit is a sign of how fast China is changing. It gives me hope that you can enjoy both sides of who you are. One day you could be happy both in China and also in The United States. I wish I could see it and see what you do with your life. The best thing you can do for me is to live a full life.

XX Your mother

February 24th 2011

Lying here in this hospital bed reminds me of Ba's last days. You will only have vague memories of my father. With every visit he looked older but happy. He saw you take your first steps, listened to your first words and heard you sing to him and saw you read your first book. He had lived all his life in China and although he was with us and adored being a grandfather, he didn't belong in California. But he laughed with us before he held his chest and died. He had not told us about the heart condition. If he had, maybe it could have been treated but I have a strange feeling that he wanted to die this way. He cherished you so tenderly; you brought him such joy.

You may be American but please Sara, go every April 5th to the little plot in Berkeley where his ashes are buried. He had a great soul. There are no plaques and names on the factories he helped build but he will live on in you. One day, please go to Beijing to the cemetery near the Summer Palace and honour your grandmother. They were special people. Jia arrives tomorrow. I will ask her to take you.

March 5th 2011

You called Jia 'Aiyi' (Auntie) and she called you Su Lin. It warmed my heart to hear that. My beautiful Su Lin. Patrick was right about your name, as usual, and I was wrong. Su Lin is a poetic echo of your courageous grandmother, Bo Lin, whom I wish you had known. My mother's name meant 'Precious' and the Chinese meaning of 'fan' is 'precious', as is the love in my mother's fan. You will inherit it.

I shall be leaving you soon, as I was left, on the threshold of adult life, without my mother. I am deserting you at such an important time in your life but I love seeing you discuss university applications and career opportunities with Jia. Despite all that, I know how much I missed my mother and here I am, repeating her life. Forgive me.

March 12th 2011

Jia loves you, Su Lin. She told me how much you have made her feel at home and how you talked to her in Mandarin. I cannot find the words to tell you how proud I am of you. I hope you will visit her in Beijing. Without me, you and Patrick will be welcome in China. I'll never know if a time will come when people like me will also be welcomed back.

Unlike most of your friends, you have a passport. That's because we wanted you to see the world. Do you remember the trip we took to Europe, starting in London? You said Tate Modern was 'cool'. Paris was beautiful and we celebrated your thirteenth birthday there. But Italy – we all loved Italy – transported us back in time to the Renaissance and to Ancient Rome. But my mood changed in St Petersburg. I cried as I remembered my mother. I said to you, 'Your grandmother studied here, read Tolstoy to me and described, in great detail, pictures in The Hermitage. She wished I could see a Chekov play. I wish, so wish, she could have lived to have known you.'

March 18th, 2011

It wasn't the persecution of the intellectuals in the Cultural Revolution that killed my mother, but a drunk driver. I am not dying in a labour camp, but in a hospital bed. Such is the unpredictable nature of life. I have already lived longer than I could have dreamed in 1990. Thanks to Patrick I have a legacy: you and a body of artworks. But Patrick is grieving already. This is breaking his heart. Our love came unexpectedly into both our lives, long after we thought it possible. We are both absurdly grateful for it. Look after him for me. Treasure him.

Patrick wants you to read the memoir I have written for you, Su Lin. Once you have read it, I hope you will understand my reluctance to share my past with you and forgive me my reticence. I have given it to your father to translate. Now, thanks to Jia, you are enjoying Mandarin and someday soon you'll be able to read its beautiful calligraphy.

You may find it difficult to read of Weiwei. Patrick insisted that you know about him and how much we loved each other. If it hadn't been your father's wish that you should know about it, I would have censored my story. I have been honoured by the love of great-hearted men.

Su Lin, these are a mother's dying wishes for her cherished daughter:

I wish you to discover your inner freedom; to know yourself and to be prepared to give of yourself. I wish, perhaps selfishly, that you remember only the best of me. My dearest Su Lin, try to forgive and forget the times when I was harsh and judgemental; you have been the greatest blessing in my life. My final wish is that you will find love and be cherished, and have someone to whom you can pass Bo Lin's fan. My only regrets are that I shall not be there to see it and that Patrick is suffering. Love him always for me as well as for yourself.

Your loving mother,

Xiaodong

March 28th 2011

My dearest daughter,

This is my last letter to you. There are tears of joy running down my face. What better gift could Jia have bought with her than my painting Transition to Spring? It was the painting I showed at the first Stars show, the illegal one with paintings hung on the railings outside the National Gallery. I saw the love and appreciation in your response when she gave it to you. This is the joy of art, of freedom and of love. Thank you, thank you with all my heart.

Your fortunate Mother

Epilogue: The Changing Face of China

Wordsworth wrote '*We have one human heart.*' Understanding the experience of the generation now governing China will help us understand each other.

The first decade of the rule Mao Zedong was an improvement on what had gone before if you were a Chinese woman or a peasant farmer. From my observation, world leaders who are successful in the first years of their rule but who stay in power beyond that time often ruin their legacy. The American constitution has it about right in limiting the term of office of the President to eight years. If Mao had left office after eight years, the tragic famine and The Cultural Revolution, which provides the backdrop to the teenage years of my heroine, Little Winter, would not have happened. Similarly, his successor Deng Xiaoping could have been regarded as one of the greatest reformers of the twentieth century if he had left office after eight years. He introduced a modern economy. That China is now the world's second largest economy can be traced back to his reforms.

China had a dynastic government for 2000 years and the Chinese Communist Party behaves like a dynasty. The recent leadership appears to be pragmatic. The dynasty may still be there but the Emperor has gone. No one man rules China and even the Chairman and Prime Minister's terms of office are fixed to a sensible ten years!

Since I wrote *Brushstrokes in Time* the Government of China has announced that it will abolish the 'Education through Labour' camps. (November 2013) So there is hope on the horizon. But, in the near future, it is unlikely that they will stop locking up awkward dissidents like Lui Xiaobo and Stars artist Ai Weiwei. My country, Great Britain, of which I am proud, has changed for the better over the past one hundred years. No country is perfect because human beings are not perfect. We should remember that the idea of human rights is quite recent. It certainly wasn't part of the British mind set when we embarked on the Opium Wars in 1839 or when we ransacked the Summer Palace.

I hope that the Chinese government will develop respect and confidence in its population to allow its citizens uncensored access to information. Openness will not threaten the dynasty any more than has opening China to the world. Chance encounters, being in a certain place at a certain time, can catapult lives into involvements with epic moments in history, which no one could have imagined. Although the character of Little Winter is fictitious, my research and many conversations over the years with Chinese friends suggest that there were many like her who didn't considered themselves heroes but whose courage lay in staying true to their ideals.

Political Figures Mentioned in Brushstrokes in Time

Party Chairman Mao Zedong

The founding father of the People's Republic of China from its establishment in 1949, he governed the country as Chairman of the Communist Party of China until his death in 1976.

Premier Zhou Enlai

He was the first Premier of the People's Republic of China, serving from 1949 until his death in January 1976. Zhou served under Mao Zedong and was instrumental in consolidating the control of the Communist Party's rise to power, forming foreign policy, and developing the Chinese economy. A skilled and able diplomat, Zhou served as the Chinese foreign minister from 1949 to 1958, advocating peaceful coexistence with the West.

Chairman of the Peoples Republic Liu Shaoqi

Head of State from 1959 to 31 October 1968. He fell out of favour during the Cultural Revolution because of his perceived 'right-wing' viewpoints and because Mao viewed Liu as a threat to his power. He disappeared from public life in 1968 and was labelled China's premier 'Capitalist-roader' and a traitor. He died under harsh treatment in late 1969, but was posthumously rehabilitated by Deng Xiaoping's government in 1980.

Vice Chairman of The Communist Party of China Lin Biao

He was the military leader who helped create the cult of Mao until his downfall in September1971.

Deng Xiaoping

He was the politician and reformist leader of the Communist Party of China who led China towards a market economy. He died in 1997.

Jiang Qing

Mao's fourth wife, a former actress, played a major role in the Cultural Revolution (1966–76) and in the creation of the radical political alliance known as the Gang of Four of which she was the leader.

Wei Jingsheng

The chapter on the trial of Wei Jingsheng is based on his autobiography The Courage to Stand Alone: Letters from Prison and Other Writings (1998)

The Stars (Xing xing)

Little Winter is fictitious, but the following are ten of the real Stars.

Huang Rui (born 1952)

One of the chief organisers: Abstract painter and publisher of the avant-garde magazine *Today*. Huang Rui was a vocal advocate of the 798 Art Zone in Beijing. In March 2004, he co-curated Thomas J. Berghuis *Transborder Language*, part of the First Dashanzhi International Art Festival which combined poetry, installation and performance art.

Ma Desheng (born 1952)

One of the chief exhibition organisers. A victim of polio, he was a self–educated artist. He made the speech at the beginning of The Stars March to Tiananmen Square and led the way on his crutches. Now living in Paris.

Qu Leilei (born 1951)

The Museum of Modern Art in Tokyo bought his Stars paintings. He recorded the trial of democracy leader, Wei Jingsheng, when working as a lighting technician for China TV. He left China for London in 1985 and became a professional artist and exhibited at *Never Forget* at Centre Pompidou, Paris in 1989. He had the first one man show by a living artist in The Ashmolean, *Everyone's Life is an Epic* (2005), and a one man show in the China National Art Museum (Beijing) in March 2011.

Wang Keping (born 1949)

A sculptor whose wooden sculptures were overtly political. He married a French woman shortly after the Stars exhibition and left China to work and live in France.

Li Shuang (born 1957)

Her marriage to a French diplomat led to political tension between China and France when she was imprisoned for two years. Later an agreement between two countries led to her release. This incident led to reform regarding interracial marriage in China. She left for Paris but, in 2010, had a solo exhibition *Butterfly Dream* inspired by Zhuangzi's Daoist classic @ Dialogue Space in Beijing.

Ai Weiwei (born 1957)

Ai Weiwei went to the USA in 1981 but returned in the nineties and developed the conceptual art scene in Beijing. He designed the Bird's Nest Stadium. His support of the parents of the victims of the Sichuan earthquake in 2008 led to persecution by the authorities. The most famous of The Stars: his 20 million *Sunflower Seeds*, referred to by Little Winter in this novel, filled the Turbine Hall of Tate Modern in 2010.The first feature length documentary film about him was *Never Sorry*.

Zhong A Cheng (born 1949)

A novelist & screenwriter, A Cheng left China in 1987 for the USA but has returned and is now living in Beijing.

Bo Yun (born 1948)

Unlike many of The Stars, he stayed in Beijing where he is now a professional painter and Professor at Tsinghua University.

Shao Fei (born 1954)

Artist and skater who was married to the Nobel Prize nominated poet Bei Dao. She left China in 1988 to join him in exile but later returned to China where she lives and works near Beijing.

Yan Li (born 1954)

He is an avant-garde poet and painter now living in the USA.

Lightning Source UK Ltd.
Milton Keynes UK
UKOW04f1057100116

266091UK00003B/43/P